# SWITCHED-ON
# KIDS

Written by Dr. Dorte Bladt, Chiropractor

Illustrations by mbwoicek

Copyright 2016, Dorte Bladt.

Not to be copied whole or in part without authorisation.

Design: aleesha.net. Printed in Australia by Printcraft.

ISBN 978-0-646-95043-3

# 1

# 2

# 3

# 4

# THANK YOU

This book is a work of passion, the result of my desire to share the message of how powerful parents can be. I am a chiropractor, not a writer, and could never have accomplished this on my own.

I want to thank Maggie for her lovely artwork, Anne, Nimrod and Tim for their wisdom working with my words, and Signe and Emil for being the source of so much joy and inspiration.

# 1

## Dream children

What a lucky child you have.  Seriously, the fact that you are taking the time to learn as much as you can about your child's health and wellbeing, and actively seeking information to help your little one be their best is fantastic, and I want to congratulate you for your dedication and devotion.

It's not easy trying to figure out what's going on with our kids. Questions play on loop in our minds as parents: Is this behaviour normal? Are they just going through 'a phase', or is this something we need to address now? How can we best help them? And what should we do specifically?

I created this book because it was exactly what I needed many years ago when I laid awake for endless hours at night worrying about my daughter and her future; I needed something that would empower me with the knowledge and skills to help my little girl be the very best she could be. You will find the answers to many of your questions in this book, compiled from my personal experiences as a Chiropractor and a mother, supported by background theory, ideas and suggestions, as well as practical tips to help your child succeed in all areas of his life. (Throughout the book I will be using him/her/he/she interchangeably; please don't let this detract from the messages.)

Thank you so much for taking this first important step to helping your child. Even though you may not hear it from her, rest assured she will appreciate your efforts, as will teachers, friends and colleagues and certainly, yours truly.

## DREAM CHILDREN

**When you watch your child sleeping – no matter what trouble they have given you throughout the day – your heart overflows with love and gratitude.**

What thoughts run through your mind as you gaze at your beautiful, resting child? What are your hopes, wishes and dreams for his future? These are the types of questions I ask of parents at the talks I run. Surprisingly, the answers are often very similar:

'We want our children to be happy, healthy, confident, resilient and capable adults. We want them to know right from wrong, to have good relationships, to be empathetic, creative and to have fun. We want them to succeed at whatever they choose to do for a living and to find a kind and caring partner to enjoy life with. And then.... hurry up and have some kids of their own so we grandparents can spoil them rotten!'

So how do we as parents ensure that our children achieve all these wonderful things in their lives?

Most of us put much thought, effort and money into making their lives as smooth and successful as possible. We love them, guide them and provide boundaries. Some of us focus on nutritious food and ensure they get plenty of exercise. Others research day care centres and suitable school systems to meet their individual needs, and some emphasise the importance of play dates, piano lessons and family time. We do whatever we can to help our children learn, develop and be happy. Yet still, what I hear time and time again from parents is this statement:

*"I feel like I'm not doing enough"*

# AM I DOING ENOUGH?

You may be worried about your child's health if she is suffering recurrent colds, flus, asthma or ear infections. You may be concerned about her performance at school; that your child is not learning as easily as you would like or not listening or maintaining concentration well.

Maybe you fear that she is not connecting and interacting as comfortably or confidently with other kids and adults as you think she should be.

*That is exactly the situation I found myself in many years ago.*

We thought our beautiful daughter Signe was an angel. She was the tiniest little cherub with wavy blonde locks and bright blue eyes. She loved singing, dancing, painting and doing craft, and she was a real chatterbox, sharing her thoughts, questions and observations with anyone who would listen – the young and old, known or unknown.

At five years old, my big girl started school. She looked gorgeous in her blue and white checked school dress. I was so proud of her, venturing out into the big wide world all by herself.

However, within a few months our world was turned upside down. The kindergarten teacher informed us that Signe had trouble with learning at school. She wasn't learning to read, couldn't do maths, wasn't paying attention and she was uncoordinated. My husband and I wondered what we had done wrong? We thought we had done everything 'right' to raise a healthy and clever little girl, including regular chiropractic adjustments, healthy foods, lots of time to play, plenty of exercise, reading and singing every day – and of course, much love.

Signe's struggles with school weren't limited to the classroom, though. She would tell me how she spent recess and lunch sitting alone on the bench while the other kids played because she couldn't run fast enough to be part of their games. When I asked if she wanted to invite friends home to play, she would say the other kids didn't like her and didn't want to play with her because she was so stupid.

My heart crumbled.

Can you imagine the pain in this little girl? Five years old, failing kindergarten, feeling worthless, useless, and no good? I wasn't feeling much better myself. In my mind, I was a failure both as a Chiropractor and a mother.

# BECOMING AN ACTIVE PARTICIPANT

The school system and the many professionals I consulted provided very little in terms of action plans and solutions so I decided I needed to become an active participant in helping my daughter to learn and feel better about herself.

Realising that I didn't have the faintest idea how, I threw myself into research. I read, did courses and studied to all hours of the morning to find ways to help my daughter succeed in all areas of her life. As I learnt about neurology, sensory motor integration, nutrition, teaching approaches and different chiropractic techniques, I practiced it with Signe. I am happy to say that what I learnt over those following *many* years has had the most profound effect on Signe's life, particularly her learning and development.

She grew from strength to strength and from success to success: academically, socially, physically, mentally and emotionally. The 'real' Signe blossomed in front of my husband and I.

No longer that young, fragile five year old, Signe is now a confident and happy young adult. She finished school with flying colours, became an excellent swimmer and has a bunch of lovely friends. Life is good! She is passionate about learning and is studying to become a primary school teacher. Along the journey, Signe empowered herself with the knowledge and tools to expand her own development and knows intimately what it is like when learning doesn't come easily. She is going to be the most wonderful teacher; I just know it.

# SHAPING SWITCHED-ON KIDS

**Working closely with Signe during those early years of her development, I became so inspired and passionate about the improvements I observed and experienced in her, I completely changed the way I practiced as a Chiropractor.** I started to care for children with all sorts of challenges such as ADHD, ADD, autism, learning problems, sensory processing disorders and so on. I worked with each child in exactly the same way as I had with Signe. Happily, most of the kids also benefitted greatly as well.

*Chiropractic care is about helping the nervous system (brain, spinal cord and nerves) work as well as possible and is really important for a child's brain function and development. Oxygen, movement, food, rest, love and connection are all important as well.*

This book is about how to best provide the brain with these essential elements, both in kids who struggle with learning, behaviour and attention, like my daughter, and all other children too. The great thing is that you don't need your chiropractor or other health practitioner to do all this for you; there are so many things that you as a parent can do at home that will help your child develop, learn and succeed in life. That is why I have written this book, to empower you to help your child be their best. The information, advice and practical tips provided here will help your child's brain develop and function optimally and will support chiropractic adjustments for the greatest impact.

Seeing the improvements that first Signe, and then many other kids realised, made me want to share my work; I knew I could help others learn to help children in their communities.

For many years now, I have been teaching this information and these techniques to Chiropractors at my Switched-on Kids seminars all over the world. It is just as important though that you – the parent - have access to this information to help you understand how your child's brain works and what you can do at home to help it function better.

I also want you to remember you are already providing your child with what he or she needs the most – your love and attention. Everything you do on top of that is an added bonus!

# 2

## Meet the boss

"I've got the brain of a four year old. I'll bet he was glad to be rid of it"

~ Groucho Marx

# The brain is the master control system of our bodies, connected to every cell, organ and system via the spinal cord and the nerves.

The nerves continuously monitor what is happening in every nook and cranny of the body and keep the brain informed about what is going on. The brain takes in all the information, processes it, compares it and sends signals back to the body about what actions need to take place. This way the brain controls and coordinates every function in the body and adapts the body to the environment. When this system is working as it is supposed to, we are healthy, happy and functioning as well as we possibly can.

However, things can go wrong, causing 'static' or interference in the messages between the brain and the body. The messages can become inaccurate, and so the brain has to make decisions based on inappropriate input. The brain can also become overwhelmed or not connected properly, and therefore not deal with the incoming messages correctly. As a result, the messages back to the body will not provide the optimum response in the organs, cells or systems. The whole system gets thrown off kilter, both in the body and in the brain, and that's when we do not function at our best and are not as healthy as we possibly can be.

This is what chiropractic is all about; detecting where the brain and body are not connecting well, causing interference in the messages. When the nervous system is not working properly it can cause the body to take on defensive postures (safe mode), which can cause harm. The brain and spinal cord are protected by the vertebrae of the spine and the bones of the skull and these defensive postures may result in abnormal movement or tiny twists in those bones. This is what Chiropractors call a *subluxation*.

Chiropractic adjustments work to reduce the nervous system 'static' or interference, allowing the body to correct the abnormal spinal and/or skull bone movement. This helps the brain to integrate and process information correctly and to send more appropriate messages back to the body about how to function. Chiropractic allows the whole system to connect better so it can heal itself and function as well as possible. The adjustments consist of very gentle stimulation to the affected spinal segments and skull bones and are specifically tailored to each individual depending on their size, age and presentation.

There are other very important ways to help the brain and body function optimally including exercise, nutrition and breathing, which will be covered later. Before we dive into how to help the brain function at its finest, let's look at how the brain and nervous system develop and function.

# Some interesting facts about the brain

**In early pregnancy, our** nerve cells (*neurons*) develop at the mind-staggering rate of 250,000 neurons per minute. This means that at birth we have 100.000.000.000 – one hundred billion – nerve cells in the brain. If you were to stack one hundred billion pieces of paper on top of each other, the stack would be about 8000 km high. That's the distance from Sydney to Tokyo – a ten hour flight.

**The number of connections** between the nerve cells increases from 50 trillion to one quadrillion during the first month of life. Already at this early stage of life there are more connections in the baby's brain than there are stars in the known universe. If your baby's body size increased at that same rate, your four kilo new-born baby would weigh 80 kilos at one month of age.

**The brain prunes** unused and under-used connections between nerve cells severely, so an older child and adult will actually have fewer connections between the neurons than a baby. However, the connections and pathways that **are** used will get bigger, faster and have better protection, and will therefore function more efficiently.

**Pathways in the brain are constructed** by nerve cells that do similar tasks bunching together. *'Nerves that fire together, wire together'* (Hebb 1949). They receive protection and insulation from other fatty nerve cells (*glial cells*) that roll around them (called *myelination*), similar to the plastic around an electrical cord. This helps to increase the speed of nerve message transmission. The more that nerves and pathways are used, the more insulation they will receive. The insulation of nerve cells causes the brain to be very fatty; the brain actually consists of 60% fat.

**Nerves can** transmit messages at speeds up to 119 metres per second.

**The brain receives** two million messages per second. We are consciously aware of only seven!

**The adult brain weighs** about 2% of our total body weight, but uses 20% of the body's energy and oxygen.

# THE HUMAN
# BRAIN PYRAMID

The human brain is built like a pyramid where the higher thinking functions such as reading, algebra and empathy depend on the proper development of previously developed brain functions, such as being able to breathe, eat, move, assess for danger, see, hear, speak and have emotions.

The pyramid development idea was introduced in the sixties by physician and neuroscientist Paul D. MacLean. He thought of the brain as the *Triune Brain*; three interrelated and integrated sections, which showed its development through evolution. He called the three parts the *Reptilian Brain*, the *Paleomammalian Brain* and the *Neomammalian Brain*.

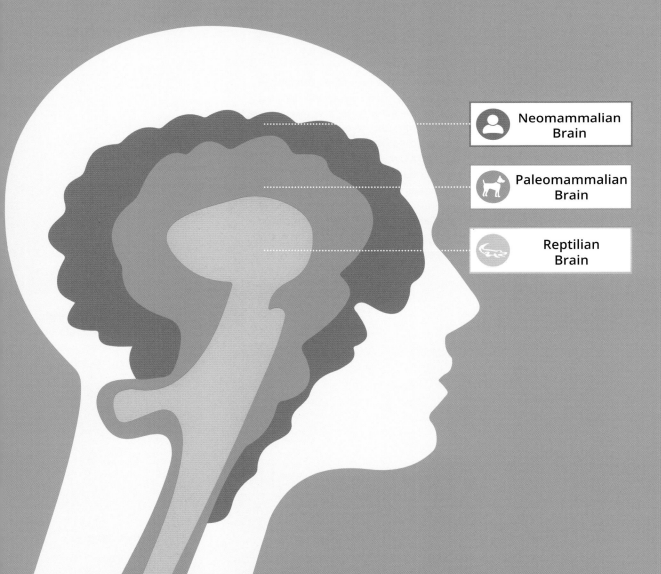

Neomammalian Brain

Paleomammalian Brain

Reptilian Brain

# REPTILIAN BRAIN

 # PALEOMAMMALIAN BRAIN

The Reptilian Brain is the automatic, instinctive part of the brain, which consists of the brainstem and the cerebellum. This is the oldest evolutionary part of the brain, which we humans share with all animals, including fish, frogs and alligators. The Reptilian Brain is the first part of the brain to develop in the womb, starting already at three weeks after conception. It is in control of our blood pressure, heartbeat and breathing rate and is responsible for our ability to swallow, sneeze and laugh.

This part of the brain it is all about 'me' and my survival: safety, food, shelter and reproduction. *'Can I eat this thing or will it eat me?' 'Am I safe here?'* or *'You are in my territory!'*

The Reptilian Brain is all about *homeostasis*; the process of always having balance in our body systems depending on the presenting circumstances. An example of homeostasis is our core body temperature remaining the same no matter what the weather is doing. If it is hot, our bodies will shunt our blood close to the surface of the skin to cool it and thereby help cool our core. If it is cold, the blood will stay close to the centre and our muscles will contract to exert themselves and produce heat. Through homeostasis the Reptilian Brain also controls our blood pressure, heartbeat and breathing rate.

The Reptilian Brain receives the sensory information from the body: touch, taste, hearing and seeing. It also receives information about where our heads, bodies and limbs are in space and which direction everything is going. The brainstem monitors our world and sends on the information to the higher centres in the brain for interpretation and decision-making. The primitive reflexes – the very basic, automated movement patterns we are born with to ensure our survival as a baby – come from the Reptilian Brain. It is the main brain area we 'live' in for the first 15-18 months of our lives.

The next brain area to develop in evolution was the Paleomammalian brain, also called the Mammalian brain or limbic system. This is the brain we share with other mammals such as cats and dogs. Here we start taking control of our world through voluntary movements in gravity and postural reflexes. We purposefully reach out for things, we learn to roll, walk and jump. The inborn primitive reflexes from the Reptilian brain get integrated into postural reflexes as the Mammalian Brain starts to develop. The postural reflexes are automatic movements which make sure we are centred the 'right way up' and they help protect us from injury if we get off-centre. For example, our arms automatically stretch out to protect us if we fall. Our postural reflexes and our voluntary control of movement start developing within the first few months of our life.

The Mammalian Brain is responsible for developing our understanding of our individuality. The child suddenly realises that she is not part of mum; or rather, mum is not part of her. Your maturing daughter begins to recognise that she is a separate person and can assert her own free will. This is when you will start to hear *'Me do it!'* or *'Mine!'* around the house. Whether she can do it, or if the toy is actually hers is not as important as her pointing out that she is in charge of the situation.

It is also the part of the brain where we begin to understand our emotions and the power of them, and also where we determine the intensity of our stress response. The Mammalian Brain is the part of the brain which is responsible for the temper tantrums in the middle of the supermarket because the grapes are green when the toddler wanted them orange. Although parents find this period very stressful – our little angels suddenly turn in to little terrors – it is an important part of their development, and should occur from around 18 months to three years of age.

The Mammalian Brain has 'way stations' for our vision and hearing. This is where we develop language and form long-term memories. Prior to this we were not able to make conscious memories, although we will still have plenty of subconscious ones.

Developmentally, we 'live' in the Mammalian Brain from around 15 months to about four years of age.

# 👤 NEOMAMMALIAN BRAIN

The Neomammalian Brain is also called the *neocortex* or *cerebral cortex*. This is the human brain; the most recent evolutionary addition to our brain. It makes up 25% of the total brain volume and contains 85% of the neurons. The neocortex is the command centre. It interprets all our senses, allows us to form complex memories, to reason and solve problems and to interpret sounds and visual images. This is where our formal learning takes place, where we acquire language, understand symbols such as letters and numbers, make decisions as well as feel empathy, analyse information and decide right from wrong. Busy, busy!

The cerebral cortex is made up of two separate halves called hemispheres, which are joined by a thick band of nerve cells, known as the *corpus callosum*.

*You may already have an idea of how the right and left sides of the brain work.*

The right hemisphere is spatial, artistic, creative and musical. It works with the 'whole picture' by using images, colour, movement, rhythm, intuition, patterns, non-verbal language and three-dimensional shapes. It inhibits behavioural impulses and can be a bit on the depressive side.

The left hemisphere is responsible for details and processes information in a linear fashion. It is logical and has drive and ambition. It is about manual technique, sequences, analysis, discrimination and verbal language. It initiates behaviour and it is what motivates us to take action and to reach our goals.

In reality, we don't rely on just one side of the brain for anything. All tasks are the result of cooperation between both hemispheres, with integrated streams of information crossing the corpus callosum. We do have a dominant brain side though, depending on the situation we are in. (For example a person may be left-dominant in analytical situations and right-dominant in social situations.) This is what makes each of us unique and provides different ways to view a challenge and solve it.

## Left hemisphere

- analytical
- detail
- linear processing
- logic
- drive
- ambition
- sequences
- motivation
- discrimination
- goals
- action
- verbal language
- manual techniques

## Right hemisphere

musical

non-verbal language

spatial

3D shapes

creative

the 'whole picture'

colour

patterns

movement

artistic

rhythm

images

intuition

To encourage both brain halves to communicate and cooperate well, they have to be strongly connected across the midline. This connection begins to develop very early on when your baby starts to voluntarily use both sides of his body at the same time. This is the case when your baby reaches for an item, crosses her midline with hands and feet and starts to cross-crawl.

We 'live' in the neo-mammalian brain from the age of four years old onwards. This doesn't mean we have out-grown the other brains and won't use them; they are always active and are essential for our survival. It just means that by this age we have the capacity to learn our human skills, which we use forever.

 CEREBELLUM

*As mentioned, according to the Triune Brain, the cerebellum is part of the Reptilian Brain. However, the function of the cerebellum is very special and deserves an explanation on its own.*

The cerebellum is the 'little brain in the back of the head, which controls the big brain in front'. It receives information from our body about where we are in space and what our muscles are doing. It coordinates our movements, posture, balance and muscle tone. Muscle tone is the slight contraction always present in our muscles, even when at rest, which prepares our muscles for movement and ensures the smoothness of movement throughout the full range of our movement.

The cerebellum is connected by big nerve pathways to the major centres of the brain: to the brainstem in the Reptilian Brain, to the Mammalian Brain and to the neocortex, and it is essential for the function of the entire brain. The cerebellum monitors the movements of the body and informs the rest of the brain about what is going on. It coordinates the commands received from the rest of the brain about what movements it wants us to perform. Essentially, it is the connection centre linking the functions of the body and the brain.

The cerebellum is crucial for short-term memory, attention, impulse control, emotion and higher cognition (like learning to read and analyse information). In fact, cerebellar dysfunction has been documented in dyslexia, dyspraxia (Developmental Coordination Disorder), ADHD, Autistic Spectrum Disorder and schizophrenia (1).

# MEET **LUKE**

Luke was a gorgeous, happy five year old who came to see me at my chiropractic practice a few years ago. Luke is a real live wire who never stops! Mum and dad were not too concerned when he was younger: *'We thought he was a REAL boy. Great at sports, very strong; he just did not like to sit still.'* However, recently they had become worried that something wasn't quite right. Luke was constantly running, climbing and moving, stressing his little sister and the rest of the family. He didn't sit for dinner, to read a book, play with toys or watch a movie. At preschool he couldn't sit still and listen at story time or take part in painting or craft activities. With BIG school next year, the preschool had recommended that Luke come to see me for a check- up.

The results of Luke's check-up were a huge surprise for mum and dad. He was very good at running, jumping, kicking and catching, just like they had told me. However, when we slowed his activities down, Luke could not balance on one foot, he couldn't stand still with his feet together when his eyes were closed, nor could he walk heel to toe in a straight line. These are all functions the cerebellum is in charge of so it looked like Luke's cerebellum was not working as well as it should have been.

I checked Luke's spine and found that he had several subluxations (vertebrae which were not moving optimally), which interfered with the information travelling between his body and his brain. When I started giving Luke gentle chiropractic adjustments to help restore this connection and improve the nerve information between the brain and the body, Luke's brain function started improving. The first thing Luke's parents noticed – and appreciated more than anything – was his connection to and communication with the family, especially at dinnertime. It was like he finally became a member of the family. His ability to balance, to concentrate and do fine motor skills also vastly improved. The preschool commented that he took part in the quiet activities, and the fridge at home started to fill up with his colourful artwork.

## PYRAMID DEVELOPMENT

*Normal brain development will happen through the progression of the Triune Brain from the Reptilian Brain at the bottom to the Neocortex at the top.*

We start out in life helpless, with just a few reflex movements hard-wired to make sure we can feed, breathe and move our neck, body and limbs. As we practice these movement patterns during the first few months of life we stimulate the next level of the brain to develop. This is when we start to understand who we are and decide for ourselves which movements we perform. By practising this for many years we finally start learning to control our movements so well that we can perform complex movements and balance. Our 'top brain' has been primed and stimulated so well that we are then ready to start taking on school learning. In essence, our body movements are what develop, arouse and connect the brain.

To learn with ease, to concentrate, to behave and to understand right from wrong requires that we progress properly through the brain pyramid of development. The premise of this pyramid is that we spend enough time at each developmental stage and receive and process sufficient stimulation to build a solid foundation for the next stage of development. This stimulation comes through movement, touch, sight, sound, smell and taste – not just as babies, but at all ages.

Sometimes things go wrong though and we may end up having gone through one of the layers of development too fast or in some cases, not at all. Because of the wonderful ability of the brain and nervous system to learn and change, this is not the end of the world. It is possible to go back at a later stage and help the brain patch the foundation of the pyramid if needed. We will talk a lot more about this in the following chapters.

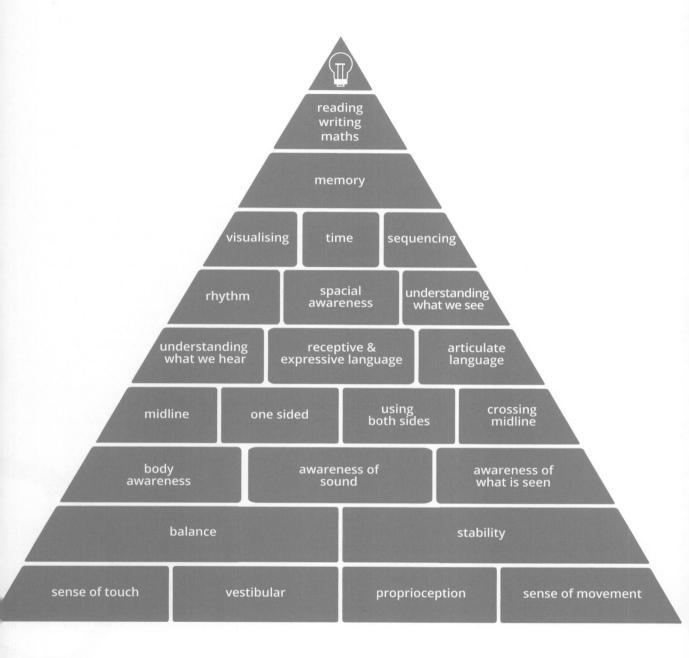

## HOW IT CAME TO BE

*So how did we end up developing our neo-cortex, our human brain? One theory suggests that it came about because we evolved to walk upright on two legs (2).*

About six million years ago, our ancestors in Africa were happily swinging around in the jungle having a lovely time singing along to Hakuna Matata. Then something huge happened (Global Warming?) and the jungle started to disappear and give way to savannah. Evolution is all about survival and conservation of energy, and we had to do something different for our species to survive. Over the next four million years our mode of transport changed from tree-swinging and knuckle-walking to walking upright on two legs. This posture enabled us to run faster over longer distances, freed our arms to carry our babies and allowed us to use our hands to perform tasks. It also saved us a lot of energy, having the load of our body weight going onto passive joints rather than active muscle load.

Upright posture and movement, as opposed to walking on all fours, was much more unstable and allowed more variation in our movement patterns. As a result, the amount of feedback to the brain from the body – information about where our head, body and limbs were in space and where they were headed – increased tremendously. The brain had to make extra nerve cells to cope with the increased information. Lots and lots of them! Our body composition didn't change much – we didn't grow any extra arms, legs or tails – and the nerve cells didn't have any extra instructions to send back to the limbs. Essentially, the nerve cells had 'nothing to do'. So instead, they started connecting with each other. This interconnection particularly happened in the top part of our brain, creating the neocortex - our human brain. As mentioned earlier, this is where we dream, communicate, understand symbols, learn language, think, have empathy and much, much more. The basic nerve pathways between the body and the brain, and also within the brain, remained the same as before; we humans now just had an extra brain layer.

The point is, our human movement patterns are what originally built our ability to read and have abstract thought. Our control of movement and balance as well as our ability to concentrate and do maths all comes from the same new part of the brain. For example, a child who has problems coordinating his movements will often struggle to learn and concentrate as well. Improving coordinated movements through practice may also improve the ability to concentrate and learn.

## BABY BRAIN

We are born with a very small and very immature brain, and thank goodness for that! Giving birth is difficult enough with a baby-size head. Incredibly though, in that little baby brain we have pretty well all the nerve cells we will have for the rest of our lives. As immature as it is, we are capable of doing so many things from the moment we are born: we can breathe, feel, search for and find the nipple to suckle, we can communicate our hunger and discomfort, we can recognise significant people by smell and sound and we can see. However, all this is obviously at a very basic level and we have a lot of developing to do to get a fully functioning brain that will let us dance, speak, read and play on the computer.

As we learn, our brain develops through the stimulation we receive from our senses. We tend to think of our senses as the five we are consciously aware of: touch, smell, taste, hearing and seeing. We actually have two more senses, which are essential for the development of our brains: the *vestibular* and *proprioception* senses.

# VESTIBULAR SENSE

 # PROPRIOCEPTION SENSE

The vestibular sense detects where we, and more importantly, where our heads are in space, what direction we are going and how fast we are travelling. The vestibular sense works by special nerves detecting movement of both the fluid and some little bones in our inner ears.

Think of being in a roller coaster, going up and down, around and around at a terrifying speed. Your eyes can't focus on anything as the world flies past. You are holding on to the railing for dear life, fearing you can't control your muscles sufficiently to keep you from flying off into space. You finally get off the roller coaster, feeling relieved, exhilarated and slightly unsteady on your feet (or possibly very nauseous). This is the ultimate vestibular experience. The fluid in the ears sloshes all around, the nerves are sending non-stop messages to the brain about where you are and where you are going, and the brain is frantically trying to get all the information together to give you a clear and concise picture of what is going on... which it can't of course, it's suffering information overload!

When you are not thrown about by a roller coaster, your brain is in total control of the situation. You turn your head to the right and the vestibular system accurately informs your brain so you know exactly how fast you are accelerating, how far from your midline you have moved, which angle your head is at, and so on.

Proprioception is about knowing where our body and limbs are in space, how fast and which direction they are travelling and under which load. Proprioception comes from special sensory organs within our joints and muscles. Stand up for a moment please, with an empty cup in your left hand, your arms along your side. Now close your eyes and touch the tip of your left little finger to the tip of your nose. Did you have any problem with that? Most likely not, as the brain received the correct information from the sensory organs in your left arm about the extra contraction needed to hold the cup while taking the best path towards your nose.

Because we live in gravity, everything we do causes our muscles to contract and resist the earth's pull. The vestibular and proprioceptive senses have to provide continuous feedback to the brain about where we are in space, what we are doing and how much the individual muscles are contracting. All of this gives the brain constant stimulation, keeping it aroused and alert. Even from within our own mother's tummy, our inner ear and muscle sensors sense movement and direction, sending constant messages to keep the brain informed of what we are experiencing. The brain depends on this constant stimulation to develop, starting from the bottom of the brain and up.

*The brain depends on this constant stimulation to develop, starting from the bottom of the brain and up.*

**Dr Dorte Bladt** 21

# SENSORY PROCESSING DISORDER

Some kids have a lot of trouble with the sensory information coming in to their brain - both the information they are sensing from inside their own body (vestibular and proprioception) and the information from the world around them – they just can't keep this information straight.

This can cause them to feel totally overwhelmed by what they are experiencing through their senses and they may try to avoid the input. Other kids seem like they can't get enough; they continually have to move, create noise or challenge their physical limits just to feel 'normal'.

# MEET **WILL**

Will came in to see me for a 'Before-Big-School' check-up.  He had been diagnosed with Hypersensitive Sensory Processing Disorder by his Occupational Therapist, who he had been working with for some time, and his parents were happy with his improvement.  However, he was still very, very sensitive to sounds, movement and touch.  Mum could not blow-dry her hair when Will was home and if the vacuum cleaner needed to be used, he would run into his room, slam the door, hop into bed and cover his head with both the pillow and the doona.  Will hated the tags on his clothes and disliked the sensation of new, 'itchy' clothes. He didn't like to be held or cuddled.  What was hardest for Will was his 'fear' of movement. He felt very uncertain about his stability in space and ability to control his movements. He was very slow and uncoordinated when trying to run and couldn't balance or hop.  He didn't like playground equipment and refused outright to try to ride a bike or a scooter.  His behaviour, when encouraged to participate in such activities, ranged from whingey and clingy to complete all-out temper tantrums, actually hitting and screaming at his parents and preschool teachers.  It seemed he would do anything to avoid whatever activity he was unsure of.

Will's mother had gone through a tremendous amount of stress when she was pregnant with him; her own mother was diagnosed with and passed away from an aggressive cancer. The birth had been a nightmare that ended in an emergency caesarean section.  Will had been a very unsettled little one with colic and reflux. He was constantly on the breast, but didn't actually like to be held.

Will had a subluxation in his neck causing interference in the nerve messages sent between the brain and the body.  This was creating havoc with Will's brain's ability to integrate the sensory information it was receiving from his body, causing Will to feel confused and overwhelmed.

Over the next few weeks, as I gently adjusted Will, his brain began to perceive his world better.  He became more confident with his movements, started to show interest in learning how to ride a bike and had fewer emotional meltdowns.  He progressed so far he was even capable of running the vacuum cleaner.  And when the time came, starting school was a breeze.  He proudly came in and showed me his new school uniform, crinkly new, with tags and all, and told me how much fun it was to be part of the school musical!  What a great new life for Will!

# PRIMITIVE REFLEXES

As mentioned, babies are born with inbuilt movement reflexes and patterns, called primitive reflexes. These reflexes develop in the womb and help the foetus to practice the movements needed for survival, such as breathing, sucking and moving the neck. The primitive reflexes make the foetus move in ways to help him actively participate in the birth process when the time comes. We have also discussed the brain needing movement as a stimulation to develop, and initially this is performed reflexively through these primitive reflexes.

 Look at **switched-on-kids.com.au** for more information

**A normal, healthy baby will have quite a few of these reflexes present at birth:**

- Rooting
- Sucking
- MORO (Startle)
- Palmar
- Plantar
- Babinski

- Asymmetrical Tonic Neck Reflex
- Symmetrical Tonic Neck Reflex
- Tonic Labyrinthine Reflex
- Spinal Galant

*Let's look at the startle reflex or MORO as it is called. I'm sure you will recognise it.*

# MORO OR STARTLE REFLEX

When a baby is surprised or scared, for example by mum moving him quickly or the dog barking loudly, he will startle: the neck will bend backwards, the arms will shoot straight up and out to protect him and he will take a quick breath in. This will be followed by the neck and arms flexing and an upset cry. The startle reflex is thought to help the newborn baby take his first breath as he passes through the birth canal. It is also helpful to protect the head should the baby fall and is a way to communicate the need for attention and assistance. The startle reflex is a 'fight-flight' reflex, a stress response, with stress hormones being released into the blood stream. This will increase the baby's heart rate, breathing rate and pulse rate and is essential for survival of the baby for the first few months of life. Then as the brain develops and the movement patterns mature, the MORO (startle) reflex movement pattern will disappear and become a less physical response.

Think of the reaction you have when someone jumps out from behind a door and screams 'BOO!' You will take a quick breath in, your neck and shoulder muscles will tense and your eyes widen in surprise. This is the adult startle response. You are not likely to throw the coffee you held in your hand on the wall behind you. The primitive reflex movement will integrate deep in the bottom of the brain and become part of the Mammalian Brain and the neocortex's reaction to surprise.

All the primitive reflexes normally disappear from view within the first few months of life. This integration – or blending with other movements - happens as a result of the baby developing her postural reflexes and the voluntary control of her movements. These movements are controlled by the Mammalian Brain and the neocortex.

Sometimes the primitive reflexes don't integrate fully, however. This can happen due to disruption of the normal brain development, which may be as a result of a difficult birth, a C-section, a fall or injury or mum's stress during pregnancy. If the reflexes don't integrate properly, it can cause long-term trouble for the child with regards to coordination, learning, behaviour and attention. The brain will continue to operate at the Reptilian, automated mode of the bottom of the brain, which prevents access to the higher centres in the brain; centres where balanced, coordinated movements happen, as well as all our cognitive, school-type learning, behaviour control, attention and immune function.

> If the reflexes don't integrate properly, it can cause long-term trouble for the child with regards to coordination, learning, behaviour and attention.

# BACK TO **WILL**

So in Will's case, his mother was very upset when she was pregnant with him, as her own mother was very ill. Will's mother had a lot of stress hormones in her system, and this exposed Will to these hormones. The result was that, from birth, Will's nervous system was primed for stress and made him hypersensitive to sensory stimuli. This caused his startle - fight or flight - reflex to be continually activated and not integrate well. The development of his postural reflexes from the Mammalian Brain was therefore delayed, causing him to be unsure of his movement control and coordination. The Mammalian Brain also helps us develop behavioural control, so Will's behaviour was very reactive and full of temper tantrums.

So when our primitive reflexes don't integrate properly, it is important to go back and help the body and brain reconnect at the developmental age of a baby. Chiropractic care and particular movement exercises can do this even at a much later stage, creating and stimulating pathways through the body to help the brain function better.

The primitive reflexes will never totally disappear from the brain. They will always be ready to help our survival if needed. If we have significant brain damage to the higher centres of the brain from a stroke or an injury, the reflex will re-emerge because the brainstem has taken over the emergency control of the brain.

# MEET **LUCY**

Lucy was like many of the children I have seen over the years. She was a seven year old whirlwind of activity. She was in my office because her teacher had expressed concern earlier in the year about her behaviour, confessing not being able to keep up with her anymore. The teacher had recommended that Lucy to see a paediatrician to maybe be put on medication for Attention Deficit Hyperactivity Disorder (ADHD).

To make the diagnosis of ADHD, the teacher and the family fills in a questionnaire about the child's inattention, impulsivity, hyperactivity and social interaction at school and at home. The behaviour pattern has to have been present for at least six months and have been present before the age of seven. The questions include:

## DIAGNOSING ADHD

*Your Child:*

» Often fails to give close attention to details or makes careless mistakes in schoolwork, work or other activities

» Often has difficulty sustaining attention in tasks or play activities

» Often does not seem to listen when spoken to directly

» Often fidgets with hands or feet or squirms in seat

» Often leaves seat in classroom or in other situations in which remaining seated is expected

» Often runs about or climbs excessively in inappropriate situations

» Often blurts out answers before questions have been completed

» Often has difficulty awaiting her turn

» Often interrupts or intrudes on others (for example, butts into conversations or games)

After looking at the questionnaire, Lucy's paediatrician diagnosed her with ADHD and recommended she tried Ritalin to see if it would help her settle at school. Lucy's parents agreed as they didn't want her behaviour to interfere with her classmates' learning, nor be a cause of stress to the teacher. However, the medication wasn't working for Lucy (or rather, it was working all too well). When Lucy was medicated, she would be quiet and compliant, but would not be spontaneous or get actively involved in anything. She would do what she was asked to do; as her father said, *'She was like a robot'*. The medication was also interfering with Lucy's sleep. She was losing weight and was starting to show signs of anxiety, all possible side-effects of Ritalin. Lucy had been on the medication for six months when the family decided to take her off it and she was back to her old very active behaviour when she came in to see me. Within seconds of entering my office, the toys were all tipped out, my drawers examined, books checked out and buttons and switches pushed.

Lucy's parents explained that her birth had been very, very fast, which can cause a lot of strain on the brain and spinal cord of a little one. She had settled in to breastfeeding quickly, but within the first month of life, developed severe colic and reflux. Mum was advised to stop breastfeeding and use a thickened non-lactose formula, which did help somewhat with her tummy symptoms. Lucy was frequently sick with a sore throat or a runny nose and had been like that since she was a baby. She was constantly on antibiotics. She had reached all her gross motor milestones early: rolling, crawling and walking.

When I assessed Lucy, I found she had subluxations in her spine and that her MORO startle reflex was still active, keeping her in a state of fight or flight. Unexpected sounds made her jump, she was constantly on the lookout for danger and therefore couldn't

concentrate on the task in front of her. No wonder she was diagnosed with ADHD. The reflex made it difficult for her to control her movements, particularly of her head and hands. She was uncoordinated and had trouble with drawing and writing. Also, the reflex made Lucy's adrenal glands work overtime to release stress hormones. Long-term exposure to stress hormones interferes with the function of the immune system. As a result, she was unable to fight off even the smallest cold virus and was sick all the time.

Lucy responded very well to the gentle chiropractic adjustments in her spine and her behaviour, concentration and immune function improved quickly. I also gave her some exercises to do to improve her coordination and brain function as well as help integrate the startle reflex.

 # NEUROPLASTICITY

To understand how learning happens, you need to understand *neuroplasticity*. We learn when nerve messages connect in new ways, creating new nerve pathways. And in time, by insulating these pathways (*myelination*), they become super highways of nerve conduction.

Imagine you are trying to learn to play the piano. Initially you will find it difficult to get your fingers to find the right keys and to move them in the right order. Your brain will be working overtime trying to remember what sequence the fingers have to follow to make the right tune. However, as you practice, your brain will create particular nerve pathways to make certain finger movement sequences and will insulate these. As these pathways get used more, the signals in the brain increase in speed, are more certain, and with time, it becomes easier, smoother and more enjoyable to play a nice piece of music (and for everyone else, easier to listen to!)

This creation of new nerve pathways and the insulation that follows is how we learn everything. Everything we think, feel and do is because the brain has created a pathway, which we automatically follow, and the more we do, the faster and the more secure that pathway will be. However, we can always create new pathways and start using and insulating these instead. The trendy word for this is neuroplasticity, which means that we are always able to learn, think, do and act in new and different ways, even as we get older.

And as mentioned earlier, neuroplasticity – the making of new neural connections and pathways – doesn't just happen by doing what we need to learn. Because moving and cognitive learning occur in the same part of the brain, you can help cement the pathways for reading, spelling, concentrating and behaving by moving. We will look at this in the next chapter.

# 3

## Just do it!

"Movement is life -
Life is movement"

~ Dr. Friedhelm Baisch

From the very beginning of life there is movement. The sperm travels up the fallopian tube to meet the egg. The two cells unite and start dividing into four, then eight, sixteen, thirty-two, and on and on it goes.

The cells start making protein structures, then tissues and then organs. From very early on the embryo can move spontaneously and by week five it can reflexively withdraw from perceived danger. The primitive reflex movements prepare the foetus for life in the real world and the baby perfects them after birth. Your toddler conquers his world by exploration and control of his posture and movement. Ultimately he reaches the very pinnacle of movement: his ability to balance.

Movement is what keeps us alive. The heart beats faithfully, pumping blood around the body to bring oxygen and nutrition to every cell in the body. Our breathing muscles contract and relax, allowing the lungs to fill with fresh air and expel the old stale stuff. The smooth muscles around the intestines gently move the food along by contracting rhythmically. Hormones and enzymes are released where they are needed by contracting and relaxing glands, and nerves send electrical signals at amazing speeds to connect everything to the master controller – the brain.

We are designed to move. We are designed to walk long distances to gather our foods or to run and catch it, not to toddle between the couch and the fridge or the car and back.

Dr. Roger Sperry, Nobel Prize recipient for brain research, demonstrated that 90% of the stimulation to the brain is generated by movement of the spine; 90%! It is vital for our children (and ourselves) to move in order to keep our brains stimulated and aroused, as well as our bodies working well.

**Here are some fun movement suggestions:**

- walking the dog
- splashing in puddles
- skateboarding
- climbing trees
- hopscotch
- playing tips
- stretching
- building cubby houses
- doing somersaults on the grass
- jumping on the trampoline (or bed or couch!)
- skipping rocks on the water
- frolicking in the waves at the beach
- walking or riding to and from school
- throwing a football or a frisbee
- rocking in the rocking chair or twirling on the twirly chair
- playing at the park
- washing the dog
- going for a bike, scooter, skate board or rollerblade ride
- pillow fights
- rolling or sliding down a hill (and walking back up)
- wrestling with mum/dad/sibling
- singing, dancing and performing
- mowing the lawn
- hopping, skipping, swinging, jumping, running and spinning
- washing the car
- tug of war with the pyjamas
- playing on the monkey bars
- jumping into the pool

When the word 'movement' is mentioned, most of us will visualise walking on a treadmill or the kids doing swimming lessons, playing footy, tennis, karate or dance classes. It does not have to be so serious though.

> Movement is as essential for learning as it is for life

When my children were younger, occasionally they would come home from school bickering and annoying each other, poking and teasing, stirring and irritating. They would complain about the snacks I had prepared for afternoon tea and fidget, fight and frustrate each other endlessly. I used to wonder why? Had I packed the wrong things for lunch, was it a full moon, did the teacher have a bad day or was I stressed, distracted and cranky myself? I noticed though, that those days were more likely to happen if the weather was ordinary and the kids had not had a chance to run around outside at school. Think about it for a minute: They sit quietly for six hours, concentrating and listening, doing fine motor activities such as drawing and writing. Ordinarily they will spend some energy playing tag with their friends at lunch and recess, but on rainy days they would have to stay inside and it would drive them crazy!

Once I realised this connection, I stopped blaming them and myself for their frustrating behaviour on rainy days. I started to experiment with movement instead. I would walk to school to pick them up, bringing raincoats and gumboots, and walk them the long way home to splash in all the puddles we could find. I would take them to the beach and let them run wild and wet in the rain and the waves. Sometimes we would go straight to an indoor play centre and stay until their energy was all spent, after which we would go home and enjoy the rest of the afternoon together. I suggest you give it a go. You may be pleasantly surprised!

# EXERCISE

*Another aspect of movement is that dreaded word: exercise.*

According to Oxford Dictionaries the definition of exercise is an activity which requires physical effort, carried out to sustain or improve health and fitness. It is really anything that increases our heart rate (and I'm not talking about the Boxing Day sales at the shopping mall). The difference between exercise and movement is both the intent and the effort. The walk you do on the beach early in the morning is movement if you enjoy the sunrise, and it is exercise if you are walking too hard to pay it much attention.

There is a lot of research confirming that exercise is good for our health overall. We all know that exercise increases the efficiency of our cardiovascular system, allowing more blood and oxygen to be pumped around the body, including to the brain. Exercise makes the bones and muscles strong, both the voluntary muscles of our limbs and trunk, and the involuntary postural muscles. Exercise improves our muscle tone - the slight ever-present contraction in our muscles at rest - which continuously stimulates our brain.

Exercise increases our stamina and improves the body's ability to detoxify. It decreases the effect of negative emotional stress and improves energy, mood and sleep. Exercise helps prevent many disease processes such as cardiovascular disease, cancer, depression and diabetes.

> *Exercise decreases the effect of negative emotional stress and improves energy, mood and sleep.*

# There is also a lot of research demonstrating that exercise helps kids to learn and concentrate, which we may not all know.

In his book 'Spark,' John Ratey, MD refers to one of the largest on-going studies correlating fitness and learning in children. The study has assessed over one million students in California over a ten year period. The results consistently show that fit children score twice as well on academic tests as their unfit peers.

One study showed that even a single bout of exercise – for example a twenty minute walk - improved a child's ability to concentrate and increased performance in academic testing that day. (3)

Researchers looked at physical fitness and intelligence in one million young men who entered the military service. They found that better aerobic fitness was associated with better cognitive (thinking and learning) function, whereas muscle strength was not. And interestingly, when they went back to the young soldiers later in life, they found that the fitter eighteen year olds had better educational achievements, better jobs and better socio-economic status. The researchers' conclusion was that aerobic exercise helps to increase cognitive function (4).

If you're intrigued by this, another interesting study looked at what would happen if academic classes were replaced by exercise classes in the school timetable. The researchers found that up to one hour per day substitution did not cause a decrease in academic performance. Conversely, the extra exercise resulted in the student's grade point average increasing across all subjects! The study concluded that increased physical activity contributed to improved concentration, memory and classroom behaviour as well as improved cognitive skills and intellectual performance. Exercise actually caused a relative increase in performance per unit of academic teaching time (5). Amazing!

Children who have been diagnosed with ADHD also benefit greatly from exercise. Studies show that the kids have less ADHD behaviour and better concentration and learning (6, 7). As little as 30 minutes of exercise in the mornings helped the children manage their ADHD behaviour through the school day (8).

The benefits included:

- Decreased stress, anxiety and depression

- Improved mood and positive feelings

- Improved behaviour, impulse control and compulsive behaviour

- Improved executive functioning and working memory

In one study, the researchers commented that exercise introduced a different way of behaving to ADHD children. This possibility of choice in behaviour pattern would be of great benefit to them later in life with regards to education, job selection and relationships, and this is something medication cannot provide (9).

Similar benefits are found from exercise in children diagnosed with Autistic Spectrum Disorder (ASD):

- Improved motor performance and social skills (10)

- Decreased stereotypical behaviour, aggression, off-task behaviour and elopement (11)

- Improved academic performance (12) and social behaviour (13, 14)

So exercise is super important for your child's performance in school and life, and hopefully you feel inspired to make regular movement a part of your child's daily routine. How much exercise do you think your child needs to be as healthy as possible in both a physical and an academic sense?

The Physical Activity and Sedentary Behaviour Guidelines released by the Australian government in 2012 makes the following recommendations:

· For babies, parents should provide plenty of opportunities each day for physical activities, especially supervised floor play (read: tummy time!). Keep the time your baby is restrained in capsules, car seats or strollers to a minimum.

· Children under five years old should enjoy at least three hours of physical activity per day.

· Children over the age of five (this includes adults!) should do at least one hour of moderate to vigorous exercise per day.

So you're thinking: *'That's impossible to squeeze into our busy day!'*

*One study showed that even a single bout of exercise – for example a twenty minute walk – improved a child's ability to concentrate and increased performance in academic testing that day. (3)*

Remember, exercise does not have to be walking on a treadmill, playing soccer, dance lessons or lifting weights at the gym – although these are all great activities. Exercise is any movement which increases the heart rate, so it does not have to be organised activities at all. Exercise is taking the stairs instead of the escalator or going to the park (and all the fun activities listed above), provided you put enough effort in so your heart rate goes up!

And the exercise doesn't have to go on for an hour at a time, especially for little ones. Short spurts are actually better. Half an hour here, ten minutes there all add up to create the stimulation the brain and body needs. What is important is that you are aware of your child's need for movement and that you provide plenty of opportunities for her to move and have fun.

# SCREENS

*In my opinion, the biggest obstacle you'll face when it comes to your child and movement is their preference for watching TV and playing on their electronic devices over active play-time.*

According to a report released by the Kaiser Family Foundation in USA (2010), it was found that the average child spends a total of seven hours and 38 minutes each day on electronic media including TV, DVD, computer, iPad, mobile phone, iPod and/or game consoles.  Many kids spend more time on media than they do sleeping!  They multi-task often; they are on more than one device 29% of the time.  Older children and teenagers under eighteen years spend on average a combined total of 10 hours and 45 minutes a day on media!  A whopping four hours and 29 minutes is spent each day watching TV alone, one hour and 29 minutes is spent in front of the computer and another one hour and 13 minutes is spent playing video games -- EACH AND EVERY DAY!

Apart from interfering with movement and physical activity, excess screen use means less time connecting with and talking to people, less eye contact and less practice in non-verbal cues.  It can lead to attention problems, school difficulties, sleep and eating disorders.  It interferes with social and emotional intelligence development and has been linked to loneliness and depression.  It also means less time for reading, imagination and creative pursuits.

Don't get me wrong, it is obviously important to learn the ins and outs of technology and to take advantage of all that we can learn, experience and achieve through various electronic media. We must however be conscious of the pitfalls of overuse. The American Academy of Pediatrics (AAP) makes recommendations in their 2013 Policy Statement on Media and Children, which the Australian Government has adopted.

They include:

» Screen use monitored and regulated by parents
» Screen time for children under two years old is discouraged. (Yes, that includes Baby Einstein and educational programmes. Babies' brains develop very fast at this age, predominantly from interaction with people)
» Children over two years old have less than one to two hours per day of total entertainment screen time

# MEET**OSCAR**

Oscar's mum was very worried about him when she brought him in to see me. She said he had become more aggressive, sullen and withdrawn over the previous year, and if it wasn't for the fact he was a small ten year old, she would have thought he was 'suffering' a severe attack of puberty. His grades at school were plummeting, he looked pale, exhausted and unhealthy. The teachers and school councillors had all but given up on him; they just left him to his own devices. He refused to participate in his usual after school activities and didn't want to play with his friends. He didn't talk to his siblings or eat with the family anymore. All he wanted to do was to play on his iPad, iPod or computer.

Screen use has recently been associated with addiction. 'Internet Gaming Disorder' as it is called, was introduced to the psychiatric manual DSM-5 (Diagnostic and Statistical Manual of Mental Disorders) in 2013 as a condition needing further study. Many psychologists are advocating broadening the diagnosis to 'Internet Use Disorder' (15). The addiction researchers are referring to in relation to screen use, particularly playing video games, is due to the fact that screens provide the brain with tremendous amounts of stimulation from quick moving pictures and a plethora of colours. This causes a release of large quantities of dopamine, the feel-good hormone in our brains, with potentially similar withdrawal cravings to substance abuse (16).

Research shows that the addictive behaviour affects emotional processing, executive attention, decision making, and cognitive control (17), causes attention problems (18), impedes academic performance (19), promotes violent and aggressive behaviour (19), and is reflected by poor sleep, slower emotional development, poor self-esteem and social skill problems (Melillo 2013).

I found that Oscar had spinal subluxations, which were possibly due to the posture he assumed when playing on his devices and that his behaviour and mood did improve significantly when adjusted. However, the adjustments had very little effect on his actual addiction. Waiting in my reception room, he had his earphones in as he played a game on his iPhone. When I asked if he could lie on his tummy on my adjustment table for five minutes without it, he would cry. When I would ask how he was going, the only conversation he could sustain would be about his most recent game purchase and how to play it. My suggestions to decrease time on the screen were met with angry resistance; a battle his mum didn't have the energy to keep up. I ended up referring him to a child psychologist, and with his expertise we managed to help Oscar decrease his dependence on his electronic devices. Oscar has a more rounded participation in life now, including time for friends, family and outdoor fun.

In a recent comment from the AAP (20), they acknowledge that their recommendations are not being followed by the public, and that their policies 'have to evolve or become obsolete'. In the real world 38% of children first play with a mobile device before the age of two (21) and 75% of children under eight have daily access to devices such as smart phones and tablets.

## The key message from the AAP is family participation.

 **CONSIDER THIS:**

- Encourage family discussions about the use of screens and agree on limits
- Play the video games with your children and watch the shows with your infants and toddlers
- Ensure quality content
- Turn the TV off during meal times
- Avoid the TV and internet-connected devices in children's bedrooms
- Limit electronics before school
- Remember, your children follow your example. If you want them to make changes, this is a golden opportunity to become more active and less 'wired' yourself.

When my children were quite young, maybe five and three years old, we had a very interesting experience. One afternoon, right in the middle of Playschool, our TV blew up. I mean literally: A loud bang, flames shooting out in all directions and plumes of smoke. It was spectacular! And luckily, harmless. We were not well off at this time and had to save up for a new one. This was a long time ago, even before the time of PC's (for us anyway), so we were totally screen-less. As a family we discovered that we actually loved it. We started going for more walks after school and dinner. We would go for bike rides and to the beach and the pool. We did heaps of reading, puzzles and craft. We talked more and had more friends around. We enjoyed it so much we actually decided not to buy a new TV. That was the way it was for years, until a friend decided we were just too weird and brought over her small portable TV (the screen the size of a shoe box) so the kids at least would know who Anna Anaconda was.

Now, I am not suggesting you have to go to such extreme measures. However, taking a step back and re-evaluating how your family spends your time, and prioritising connection, communication and activities that keep you moving will greatly enhance your family's health, wellbeing and learning potential.

#  BRAIN WIRING MOVEMENT

**We have talked about movement and exercise as being essential for brain function. There is another aspect to movement we need to consider when we relate movement to brain function and development: the movement patterns which helped develop the brain in the first place, from the bottom Reptilian Brain to the thinking and school-learning neocortex.**

We mentioned how babies innately know to move from the moment they are born. Their little arms and legs are flailing all over the place without any apparent control. However, right from the start there are some movements that are inbuilt in the brain: those primitive reflex movements. When the head is turned to the side, the arm and leg on the same side will straighten. When the palm is touched, the fingers will close. Our beautiful, capable babies exercise their little brains and bodies through these exquisite patterns of movement. You may remember that within a very short period of time the primitive reflex movements will start to integrate, as the higher centres in the brain pyramid start to take over. We develop postural reflexes, helping to keep us upright and protected if we get off balance, and we develop the ability to take conscious control of our movements in gravity.

These voluntary, sequenced movement patterns are controlled from above and down, inside and out (from head to toe, centre to periphery) and as mentioned, they help build the higher centres in the brain. First, the baby learns to control the head, then the trunk and lastly, the limbs. He learns to hold his head up above the body initially when lying on the tummy, then when lying on the back. She also learns to hold the head in line with the spine when held upright. He learns to roll from tummy to back, and from the back to the tummy. Your baby learns to bring the hands together in the midline and to put her toes in her mouth. Then there's the commando crawl, cross-crawl, walk, run and jump. These controlled and coordinated movements create connections between the body and the brain, forge pathways in the brain and help these pathways become fast super-highways of information, allowing the child to learn new things and become really competent at them.

Think of when you took your baby to the early childhood nurse. She would have asked you what your baby was up to: *'Is he rolling?' 'Can she sit on her own?'* And not only would the nurse measure your baby's head and weight, she would have pulled her to sitting to see if she could control her head. Do you think the nurse was really interested in how your baby could move? What she was assessing was how well your baby's brain was working because – as you've probably started to understand – movement and brain function are inter-related. Movement and cognitive learning happen in the same parts of the brain, using the same pathways. Our ability to think, control emotions, pay attention, use language, understand maths and do spelling words - ***everything*** - are all related to our body's ability to move.

The gross motor milestones don't stop with babies. We learn to walk at around one year of age, jump when we're about two, stand on one foot momentarily at three, hop about four, skip at five, balance on one foot at six and so on. Our ability to control and coordinate our movements in gravity improves with age until adulthood, giving us a window into the function of the brain.

Sometimes, for whatever reason, some little ones are not very good at performing certain movements. They may reach a movement milestone later than expected or miss it altogether. This may be an issue with the development of pathways in the brain.

Other kids seem to fly through their milestones. We as parents get so excited when our little one rolls, crawls and walks early. We proudly announce that they are really clever - which they definitely may be. However, the milestones are 'windows of opportunities' for development. If a child goes through a movement phase too fast, he may not get the full benefit of the movement pattern for the brain. What to do? We can't sit on them to hold them back, nor push them to learn.

The good news is that it's never too late. It is possible to go back later and repeat the sequential movement patterns. This will help your child's brain create and stimulate those brain pathways, and catch up on both coordination and cognitive delays that way.

# MEET **CHRIS**

Chris was a little patient of mine. He was eight years old and had been diagnosed with Dyslexia. He couldn't read. He would look at all those crazy little ants running all over the page and couldn't understand that anyone could make any sense of them at all. Chris was a lovely little boy who really tried his best, but as this wasn't good enough, he was starting to feel quite despondent and helpless.

We typically think of Dyslexia as letter and number reversals and misplacements, which can be part of the picture. A person with Dyslexia often finds it difficult to separate the individual sounds in the words, associate sounds with letters and blend sounds to make words. This makes reading, writing and spelling very difficult. A person with Dyslexia may also have trouble understanding and remembering new concepts and comparing these to something already known. The label 'Dyslexia' is not often used anymore. Instead, the school psychologist may find that the child has 'slow processing speed'.

When Chris came in to see me he was in a bad way. He was being bullied at school, both because he had trouble reading and also because he wasn't very sporty. He was clumsy, uncoordinated and slow, and his self-confidence and belief were non-existent.

Chris had had a rough entry into this world, with forceps used to help him out of the birth canal. This had caused a lot of traction force on his upper neck and he wasn't breathing at birth. Thank goodness the doctors and nurses were able to perform miracles and little Chris survived. Chris never figured out how to breast-feed. He never rolled or crawled.

When I checked his nervous system I found that he had a subluxation in the top part of his neck interfering with the nerve information travelling between his brain and body. We gently adjusted Chris over a period of time and gave him some exercises to do at home. The exercises were to help reconnect his brain; they included rolling on the floor, cross-crawling and marching. We will discuss these exercises shortly.

One day Chris and his mum came in for his adjustment early before school. They both looked like death. They could hardly keep upright. Worried, I asked if they were ok. *'Absolutely'* said Mum giving me a big kiss. *'Chris figured out how to read last night! It was so exciting. He just kept on reading and reading. We read all the Dr. Seuss books, but didn't finish till one in the morning. We are exhausted. We might go straight back home to bed today!'*

# LEARNING DISABILITIES

Dyslexia is part of a group of diagnoses related to brain processing called *Learning Disabilities*, which also include *Dyspraxia* (problems with coordinated movements), *Dysgraphia* (difficulty with writing and other fine motor skills) and *Dyscalculia* (severe math and number learning difficulty). Learning disability describes a person of normal or above intelligence who doesn't learn or process information the way educators expect.

# DYSLEXIA

Dyslexia is the most common learning disability, making up about 80% of the diagnoses.

*Little people with Dyslexia grow into big people with Dyslexia.*

According to Australian Workforce Futures - A National Workforce Development Strategy; a report produced by Skills Australia in 2010, approximately seven million Australian adults (that's 46%) had literacy scores below the minimum level needed to function fully in life and work, and 7.9 million (or 53%) had numeracy scores below the minimum needed.

# DYSPRAXIA

Dyspraxia is better known as *Developmental Coordination Disorder* and this is a motor learning/planning disability. The child knows what he wants his body to do but can't figure out how to get his body to do it so has challenges with creating smooth movements and coordination. Because the mouth and tongue are muscles, this can result in speech and articulation problems. There can also be some difficulties with perception and thought. According to the Dyspraxia Foundation of Australia 80% of people with Dyspraxia are male.

We had an experience with a friend's child who was asked to help cook on a camping trip. He was used to and very capable of peeling carrots, but when asked to peel potatoes, which involves a more rounded movement and more thumb control, he just couldn't do it. He was unable to take a movement he knew well and slightly modify it to this new situation, which could mean he has Dyspraxia. The potatoes were flying everywhere, and soon he was relieved of duty, which could have been the plan all along. I explained the possibility of chiropractic improving motor planning to his mum and she decided to take him to a chiropractor close to where they lived. I was very happy to have a willing and capable helper peeling potatoes the following year.

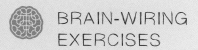

## BRAIN-WIRING EXERCISES

As you will remember, our human abilities for movement and learning take place in the same parts of the brain and use the same nerve pathways between the brain and the body. The development of skills needed for cognitive learning develops alongside our capacity for controlling and coordinating our movements. This means it is possible to train the brain to function better cognitively by doing specific brain-stimulating exercises with the body. When we do the movement patterns we possibly missed or rushed as little ones as an exercise, we build nerve pathways and connections irrespective of our current age. This is neuroplasticity, which you were introduced to in the previous chapter.

Research shows that our ability to coordinate our movements and our intelligence and learning capacity are related (22). In one study, researchers demonstrated that children with learning disabilities (reading, spelling and mathematics) had poorer gross motor skills than their peers (23). Another study found that children struggling with Dyslexia had poor balance control (a function controlled by the cerebellum) (24).

Coordination exercises have been shown to improve kindergarten children's cognitive function (25) and attention (26) in as little as 35 minutes, twice per week for eight weeks. One study looked at the effect of six months of brain-coordination exercises in children with learning difficulties and found that the children in the exercise group had significant gains in reading, writing and comprehension, dexterity and speech/language fluency, compared to the non-exercising control group (27). When followed up several years later, the children had retained the improvements they had gained in motor skills, speech/language fluency, sound organisation and working memory (28).

## BRAIN-STIMULATING EXERCISES

Following are some of the exercises I give to the children I see in my practice. They are all designed to help the brain and body connect, as well as making super strong pathways between the different parts of the brain. My suggestion is to begin at the beginning, no matter which struggles your child has and what movements he or she did as a baby. Start with the first three exercises. Do them for five minutes twice per day for the first week. Then switch to the next three exercises twice a day for the next week. Continue just like this.

If you have any questions your Chiropractor can guide you on how to put these into practice and which of these exercises will best help your child.

### Initially, some of the exercises may seem challenging for your child.

If so, break them down into smaller movements, such as only using the arms and not the legs or vice versa. Please do persevere, though. The brain will catch on. Once you have gone through a whole section, spend some weeks practicing them so your child can choose the three exercises to do that session. When your child masters the movements, you can introduce a challenge to keep it interesting, such as competition (let siblings join in), a ball to score goals with or doing times tables or spelling words at the same time.

# FLOOR EXERCISES

## Half Rolls

Lying on the stomach with the arms stretched above the head, use the stomach muscles to slowly roll the whole body up on to one side. Hold for one second. Then, again using abdominals, roll up onto the other side and hold. Roll back and forth like this twelve times to each side. If this is easy, you can hold arms down alongside the body. This makes it a little harder to lift the shoulders. Next, do the same exercise rolling from shoulder to shoulder, but lying on the back. Make sure that the movement comes from the stomach muscles, not the feet or legs.

## Log Rolls

Lying on the stomach with the arms stretched above the head, keep the body straight and use the stomach muscles to slowly roll onto the back. Continue rolling to the front again and continue this way until twelve full rolls have been completed. Then roll back the other way for twelve rolls. If you don't have space for that many rolls, or your child feels dizzy, do three or four rolls, and then go in the opposite direction. Repeat until 24 full rolls have been completed. To make this exercise a little harder, roll while keeping the arms down alongside the body.

## Segmental Rolls

Lying on the stomach with the arms stretched above the head, bend one knee to 90 degrees, lift if off the floor and move that foot and lower leg toward the other side of the body to initiate rolling onto the back. Once on the back, straighten the leg, bend the opposite knee and bring it across the body to initiate rolling onto the tummy. Do this ten times in both directions.

Then do the same exercise, but initiate the roll with the arms this time. Lie on the stomach with the arms stretched above the head and bring one arm down to shoulder height, extending away from the body at 90 degrees. Lift the arm and shoulder off the floor to initiate the roll onto the back. Once here, place that arm above the head and bring the opposite arm across the body. Lift the shoulder up off the floor and roll back onto the abdomen.

The rolling exercises stimulate the vestibular system in the brain. The brain also receives a lot of stimulation through various parts of the body being in contact with the floor (*tactile stimulation*). The core muscles have to contract to get the roll started and with the segmental rolling, we encourage crossing of the midline.

## Egg Rolls

Have your child sitting on floor with legs tucked in and the arms wrapped around the legs. Lean back and roll the body back as far as possible then use the stomach muscles and speed to roll back up. Roll back and forth on the spine twenty times.

## Seals

Lie on the stomach with the arms down along the side of the body. Lift up the head and roll one shoulder up and forward and try to pull the body up with it. Then roll up the other shoulder and try to pull the body along again. Use the movement of rolling the shoulders to drag the body along the floor. It is ok to use the toes to push the body along a bit, to help your child feel he or she is actually getting somewhere. Continue for at least two minutes.

## Inch worms

Lie on the back with arms down along the sides, both knees bent and the feet on the floor. Roll one shoulder up and backwards while pushing a little with the feet, so as to drag and push the body along the floor. Then roll up the other shoulder and continue this movement along the floor for two minutes.

## Airplanes

Lie on the stomach with arms alongside the body. Contracting the stomach muscles, lift the upper body off the floor and hold for ten seconds, building to 30 seconds as your child gets stronger. Next, rest the upper body while lifting the legs (also the thighs) ten centimetres off the floor and hold for 10 seconds, eventually building to 30. Once arms and legs can easily be done separately, lift both arms and legs at the same time, and hold for 30 seconds.

Then roll onto the back and repeat the exercise. To start with, leave the arms alongside the body. Lift the upper body like you are doing a low sit-up and hold for ten to thirty seconds. Make sure that the abdominal muscles are contracting, so the tummy doesn't 'pop up'. Then rest the upper body and lift both legs off the floor, again contracting the abdominal muscles to avoid arching the low back. The higher the legs, the easier it is to hold. Once this is achieved, try to lift both legs and upper body up at the same time. To make the exercise harder, stretch the arms out to the side (like an airplane) or hold them above the head. This exercise can be held for as long as you wish, but it is harder than it sounds (Give it a try yourself).

Egg rolls, Seals, Inchworms and Airplanes encourage core muscles to work, which will help the central muscle tone and increase overall brain function. Anyone who has done Pilates will recognise how hard these exercises are and marvel at the ability of a baby to hold these positions for minutes at a time, many, many times per day.
The exercises also stimulate the brain through tactile stimulation. Seals and inchworms also include the cross pattern movements, which connect the two brain halves.

## Commando crawling

This is a cross-crawling activity where the trunk is kept close to the floor and the elbows and knees are used to move the body along the floor. The opposite elbow and knee will move forward together. Continue for at least 60 seconds.

This exercise puts a lot of pressure on the knees and can be uncomfortable. Doing it on carpet or grass, as well as wearing long pants, will help. You can also tie something soft around the knees to take some of the pressure.

## Stop Signs

Lie on the stomach with the head turned to one side. Flex the shoulder and elbow on the side of the head facing to ninety degrees, so your child is looking at his or her thumb. The other hand rests in the small of the back. The leg on the side to which the head is turned is straight, the opposite knee and hip are flexed to 90 degrees. Now swap sides. Turn the head to the other side and move that arm so the thumb is in front of the nose. The other arm moves to the small of the back while the legs move so the leg on the nose side is straight and the other one is flexed. Keep swapping from side to side, aiming to make it one fluid movement. Continue for 60 seconds.

## Supine cross-crawling

Lie on the back with arms stretched straight over the head, touching the floor, and the legs straight down. Now lift the right arm and the left leg in the air at the same time. Return to the floor and swap sides. If this is too difficult for your child to do, you can touch the opposite arm and leg to help the child concentrate on the pattern of the movement.

Continue for 60 seconds.

## Cross-crawling

On hands and knees, move the opposite arm and leg forward at the same time. With this exercise, encourage the child to look at the forward hand, swapping eye focus from side to side. Continue for 60 seconds.

## Homo-lateral crawl

Crawl as before, but move the same side arm and leg forward at the same time.

## Standing cross-crawl

Get the child to march in a cross pattern lifting opposite arm and leg at the same time.
Do this for at least 30 seconds. Next, ask her to cross the midline and touch the hand or elbow to the opposite knee.

## Dog cross exercise

In the hands-knees position, ask your child to raise the opposite arm and leg to horizontal, in line with the trunk, and hold for ten seconds. Make sure the back doesn't arch or sink down, but that the core muscles are switched on. Repeat ten times to each side.

The cross patterns in these last exercises help the integration of the left and the right sides of the brain. All activities in the brain, including thinking, reading, maths, behaviour, emotional control and planning need input from both sides of the brain, and this movement is essential for optimal brain function for learning. Cross-crawling is essential for training the eyes to cross the midline of the body by focusing on one hand and then the other. It also trains the eyes to focus and track. Crawling combines the vestibular (where the head is in space), proprioceptive (where the body and limbs are in space) and visual systems for the first time to learn balance, space and depth perception.

Once your child has mastered these essential movement patterns, it is time to move on to some new ones. Again, I suggest you encourage your child to do the first three for the first week, then the next three. Once it is time for your child to choose, both these current exercises and the ones from the previous group are fair go.

# FINE-MOTOR EXERCISES

I often find that fine-motor weakness and poor control – such as difficulty with pencil grip and hand writing – are symptoms of things that are not working well closer to the centre of the body rather than a hand and finger problem. So initially, I recommend focusing on improving core and shoulder girdle strength, adding the fine-motor exercises later.

## Push-ups

Start by standing 50 centimetres from a clear wall, with hands placed on the wall at the level of the shoulders, with a 90 degree bend in the elbows. Keep the hands flat on the wall, with the fingers spread out. The feet should be approximately shoulder width apart. Push away from the wall until the elbows are straight, while keeping the body totally straight, the head in line with the spine and no arching of the lower back. Slowly flex the elbows to lean the head and body towards the wall, and stop just before the forehead touches the wall. Repeat ten times. Move the feet further from the wall to increase the difficulty. As shoulder and core strength improves, the push-ups should be done on the floor; initially on the knees, and then if possible, on the toes. Always make sure the spine and neck are in a straight line.

## One armed push-ups

Similar to the push-up on the wall above, but only using one arm. The focus is on keeping the body straight, not twisting or sagging.

## Jungle gym/ tree climbing/ rock climbing

Let them have fun improving shoulder, arm, hand and finger strength.

## Plank

Start by lying flat on the stomach. Bring the elbows onto the floor directly under the shoulders, with the forearms resting flat on the floor. Lift the trunk straight up with the weight on the elbows and knees. Ensure that the body is totally straight between knees and head - this means looking slightly ahead of the hands. Hold this position for 30 seconds if possible. For the next level, lift the knees off the floor and keep a straight, strong line from the toes to the top of the head.

## Wheelbarrow

Have your child on all fours on the floor. Stand behind the child and bend carefully to take hold of their legs while they take their body weight on outstretched arms. Make sure they keep their trunk in a nice straight line, indicating they are using their back and abdominal muscles. If they struggle, move your hands further up their legs, so you carry more of their body weight. Get them to walk forward on their hands. Do for 30 to 60 seconds, if possible.

## Shoulder Bridge

Lie on the back with arms on the floor, both knees bent and the heels close to the bottom. Push through the heels, contracting the buttocks, lower back and lower abdominal muscles to lift the bottom and trunk off the floor so the body weight is resting on the back part of the shoulders and the feet. Hold position for 30 seconds.

## Tug of war

Playing with a parent, friend or sibling, each pulling the opposite ends of a towel, sheet, tea towel, belt, rope or shoe lace. The gripping and pulling is excellent for improving intrinsic hand muscle and finger strength.

## Fist exercise

Playing with partner, take turns hiding a small object in a clenched fist and the other person trying to open it.

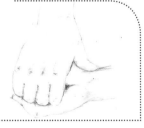

## Squishy

Fill balloons with flour, sand, salt, beans, birdseeds or rice and tie them off. No need to blow them up at all. Let your child feel, squeeze, pull, manipulate and play with the balloons.

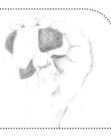

## Finger tapping

Gently touch each fingertip in turn to the tip of the thumb. Practice in both directions. Try to do both hands at the same time and each hand individually. Continue for 30 seconds with each. Then repeat with firm finger pressure.

## Thumb around fingers

Roll the thumb around each fingertip in turn. Practice in both directions. Try to do both hands at the same time and each hand individually. Continue for 30 seconds with each.

## Chinese balls manipulation

Use two large size marbles for a child's hand. Play with both marbles in the hand, trying to get one marble to move over and under the other and to rotate them in the palm of the hand, clockwise and anti-clockwise.

## Figure eight doodling

Put a little cross in the centre of an A4 size paper. Draw with a texta or a pencil initially, the number eight on its side (infinity or lazy eight). Start on the cross in the middle, draw a circle up and around, returning to the cross and then continue up and around to the other side. Continue for 30 seconds. Then change direction for 30 seconds, followed by the two directions with the other hand. Do these exercises drawing infinity in different sizes. Take up a whole page, only half or tiny little writing sizes.

## Letters on figure eight

Put a little cross in the centre of an A4 size paper. Draw with a texta or a pencil initially, each letter of the alphabet through the cross in the middle, following the path of the lazy figure eight. All the letters of the alphabet will fit this mould, some obviously starting above the cross, but going through it, some just staying in the midline. This is a great exercise for the child to get a physical handle on the different sizes of the letters.

## Eye dropper

Have two friends, a warm day, a bowl of water and two eyedroppers. Squeeze to fill the dropper and then squeeze hard and fast to squirt the other person.
Try to use both hands.

## Coin flicking

Have two children sitting at a small table. Agree which finger to use to flick against the thumb to try to get the coin over the other edge of the table for a goal.
Use both hands and all the fingers.

# 4

## Yummy, yummy in my tummy

"One cannot think well, love well, sleep well, if one has not dined well."
~ Virginia Wolf

## "We are what we eat"
### - Lindlahr

This is a no-brainer, really. We all know that from the food we ate yesterday we will build our body today. Our dinner is turned into energy for living, thinking and moving and into the new cells that are continually produced for our bodies to heal and grow. Would you rather have brain cells, blood cells and heart cells made from pizza or from broccoli?

# MEET **NICHOLAS**

I have been working with a young boy named Nicholas recently who came to my practice with behavioural problems. He is four years old and a handful! He is loud, aggressive, can't sit still and doesn't function well in a group. His appointment with me is always late in the afternoons, straight from day-care, and of course he is always hungry. His mum politely asked at the first couple of visits if it was ok to give him some food. She would then pull out a big, crackling shopping bag and let him choose between packets of flavoured chips, lollies and technicoloured chocolates.

There is no doubt in my mind that Nicholas' mum wanted the best for him. She loves him dearly and will do anything to keep him happy. She would have had her reasons for her selection, whether it was because she felt the pre-packaged treats were suitable food choices or to keep Nicholas quiet in my office. Either way, my job as a Chiropractor is to help Nicholas' brain and body function better, and encouraging healthy eating is part of that job. So over the next many visits while I was adjusting him, Nicholas and I chatted about how to build a strong body. Nicholas responded well to chiropractic care and his behaviour improved at day-care and at home. He also improved greatly because of the new food choices his family was making. He would excitedly tell me how many carrots he had eaten since his last visit, how he had tried peas and cauliflower and how he enjoyed the chicken pieces and cherry tomatoes mum packed for him in his lunch box at day-care. I never told him not to eat what I thought of as junk. We - and children in particular - are often literally addicted, both physically and psychologically, to the chemicals in our foods. Saying we can't have something just makes us focus on the want even more. Try this for a moment. Don't think about a pink elephant. Do not think about a pink elephant. Please, whatever you do, don't think about a pink elephant!!

**What are you thinking about?**
**Pink elephants, by any chance?**

It works the same with food. I can't have chips and chocolate. I am not allowed to have chips and chocolate. Why am I not allowed to have chips and chocolate? I want chips and chocolate! NOW!
It often works better by adding better choices and allowing your child to create a new, healthier habit.

## FOOD DIARY

On the topic of nutrition, there is so much to think about.

Everyone knows what good food is: natural, wholesome and un-processed foods, yet we still don't eat this way consistently. Even more puzzling, why do some people react badly to these nutritious foods? How is it that one person can thrive on a particular diet and another will struggle? How can we in the Western world have access to such a great variety of excellent foods and still many of us be malnourished? Lots of questions; read on for some answers.

*Let's start with separating fact from fiction.*

Our reality is filtered through our individual perception of the world. I have often observed that we 'think' we eat better than we actually do, just because we try so hard to do what is considered 'right'. We think we only have the occasional special treat or let the kids have only the odd lolly. We are sure we don't eat take-away very often, except for when we are really pressed for time or feel so exhausted that we can't be bothered worrying about it. However, the reality is that we feel like this a lot of the time and it soon adds up.

## LOOK AT YOUR REALITY

*Knowing the facts can be so liberating because the evidence is there in black and white. Once we have the data we can make a decision about what it is we are going to change, and then do it - one little step at a time.*

 Take a look at YOUR reality for a moment. Grab a sheet of paper and write down everything you had to eat yesterday. Every little thing!

You don't need to share this with anybody so you can be totally truthful with yourself. I know yesterday wasn't an ordinary day, that it wasn't your 'ideal' eating type of day, but do it anyway. Everything you ate for breakfast, lunch and dinner, and then everything you ate in between.

Now have an objective look at what you have documented. Does it look good? Don't just worry about your calories. You are looking at your nutrient content. What did you consume that was processed? How many servings of caffeine did you have (tea/coffee/cola/energy drinks)?

How many glasses of water? How many serves of fruits and vegetables? How many pieces of cake and chocolate? How many servings of wheat products (bread, biscuits, cereal, pasta)? How many alcoholic drinks? How much protein? How much of what you ate contained colouring, flavouring or preservatives, or all of the above?

If you are looking at your list and are feeling despondent, don't worry. You are not alone. Most of us when we do this exercise are shocked. It's not that your diet is really bad; it is those 'extra' bits that sneak in, even though we decided not to eat them. Think of it this way: at least you now know!

Now, do the same exercise for your child. Write down everything she ate yesterday, both what you served her and what she had elsewhere. When you look at this objectively, are you happy with the nutrient content of this diet or is modification needed? Could it be time for the whole family to make a change for the better?

# RECOMMENDED DIET

When I grew up, the guidelines for healthy eating were well known.  What was 'healthy' was touted from everywhere: school curriculums, supermarket brochures, handouts at the doctor's office and leaflets at the library.

The information was so commonplace, it was even printed on the back of cereal packages.

## *Do you remember the Food Pyramid?*

Yum, those were the days when you could eat cheese sandwiches for breakfast, lunch and dinner and *know* you were eating a healthy diet!  The Food Pyramid recommended a diet consisting of carbohydrates such as cereal, bread, pasta and rice as the main staple. Then came fruit and vegetables, which were to be consumed in smaller amounts.  Dairy products such as milk, cheese and yogurt were the next level up on the pyramid, and protein products, including meat, fish and eggs were at the top.  It turns out though that there is no scientific research to support this recommendation – and there never was.

The Food Pyramid was developed in the early 1900's by the American Department of Agriculture allegedly to improve people's nutrition and thereby their health.  Sceptics have said its purpose was to increase the consumption of surplus grains.

Being on the pyramid was good for business, and lobbying was intense from agricultural interest groups to have recommendations made for daily consumption.  The food pyramid is still ingrained in many people's consciousness and is probably partly to blame for the increasing levels of obesity around the world.  The reason for this is that the carbohydrates present in bread, rice and pasta are very easily digested and converted into glucose (sugar), which the body will use for energy or store as fat.

In 2012, the UN Secretary General announced that there were 30% more obese people in the world than undernourished people.  At this very moment, 63.4% of Australian adults are overweight or obese (29).  64% of adult UK citizens, (30) 69% of Americans (31) and 47% of Danes are overweight or obese (32).  More than 25% of Australian children are overweight or obese (29).

And this upsizing of our bodies is so much the norm that parents don't even perceive their overweight children as being so (33).  Rather, they look at their normal Body Mass Index (BMI) children and find them under-weight and under-nourished.

# HEALTHY FOOD

So if the Food Pyramid is not the way to go, what does a good daily diet consist of? What I recommend for adults, provided they don't have any food intolerances, is to eat fresh, local, organic where possible, and unprocessed produce:

## VEGETABLES

Five cups of different coloured vegetables and at least two of them raw (less for children, but more on that later). Variation is key, so try adding these to your usual repertoire:

- Artichoke
- Parsnip
- Asparagus
- Radish
- Eggplant
- Kale
- Leek
- Okra

## FRUIT

Two cups of different fruits (less for children). Go for what is in season, and enjoy a great mix. Try:

- Star fruit
- Figs
- Mulberries
- Dragon fruit
- Guava
- Pomegranate
- Lychees
- Persimmons
- Mangosteen

## PROTEIN

Three servings of protein, each the size of your palm:

- Meat
- Nuts
- Chicken
- Seeds
- Fish
- Quinoa
- Eggs
- Chickpeas
- Tofu
- Green peas
- Tempeh
- Beans
- Lentils
- Legumes

(If you eat dairy products, some, for example, milk, yogurt and cheese also contribute protein).

## GOOD FATS

These come from:

- Cold-pressed olive or macadamia nut oil
- Oily fish
- Avocado
- Nuts
- Seeds (flax, chia and sesame)

Daily intake could be 1/2 an avocado, a handful of nuts (walnuts, macadamia and brazil nuts are higher in omega 3), a sprinkle of seeds and two lines of oil the length of your index finger. You could also use a fish oil supplement.

## WATER

You need about 25 ml per kg of body weight. So if you have a six year old child weighing about 20 kg he should drink half a litre of water per day. A person weighing 60 kg needs 1.5 litres of water per day and a person weighing 80 kg should have 2 litres. Water means water, not juice, cordial, milk, coffee or energy drinks. The sugar, protein, caffeine and flavouring take away the cleansing properties of the water and drain the organs instead of rehydrating them. A squeeze of lemon or lime juice, or a few mint leaves can add a lovely zing to a cold glass of refreshing water. If you prefer a hot drink, herbal teas are great.

## BREAKFAST

*I am often asked about skipping meals.*

Many children (and adults as well) seem not to be able to stomach their breakfast before school. Then they are famished by midmorning, eat everything in their lunchbox all at once and end up craving energy-rich foods like chips and cakes later. Studies have shown that skipping meals causes the body to think it is starving. It slows down the metabolism of the body and is more likely to convert foods into fats to store energy for future lean times (34-35). (This does not include intermittent fasting, which is another topic.) Kids who eat breakfast learn and concentrate better at school (34, 36). Try to encourage your child to eat just a little something, even if it is as she walks to school, like a piece of fruit or a handful of nuts. This will usually help her body and brain kick into gear and carry her over until she can have something more substantial at recess.

At this point people ask: *'But where are my carbs? I need my cereal for breakfast! Where will I get my fibre?'* We do need carbohydrates in our diet because they provide glucose, which our brains, in particular, use for energy. Your vegetables and fruits will provide you with plenty of both carbs and fibre so you don't actually need them from breads, cereals or starchy additions to your main meal. You may still want them and that is ok. Just choose sources that are as unprocessed as possible, such as whole grains, brown rice and wholemeal flours.

This looks like a fairly straightforward and sensible way of eating, doesn't it? We may feel we can eat like this with minimal effort, but it is often harder than we realise. This is especially true if you have been eating lots of processed foods and carbohydrates for some time. Again, my advice to families who are trying to make healthier habits at home is to make one little change at a time. Try add-ons instead of take-aways. For example, your kids might enjoy raiding the cupboard for cakes and biscuits when they come home from school. Try to encourage them to have some carrot sticks with hummus, an egg, the leftover meat from yesterday's dinner or a piece of fruit before they have the treats.

*You may both be pleasantly surprised to find that they don't actually need or want their sweet snack*

The one thing most of us can agree on is that our daily diets need more fruit and vegetables. The Australian Government - National Health and Medical Research Council (NHMRC), as well as the Department of Health and Ageing (DoHA), recommend in their 2013 dietary guidelines that:

**2 - 3 YEAR OLDS EAT**
one serving of fruit and 2.5 servings of vegetables per day

**4 - 8 YEAR OLDS EAT**
1.5 servings of fruit and 4.5 servings of vegetables per day

**9 - 11 YEAR OLDS EAT**
two servings of fruit and five servings of vegetables per day

**KIDS 12 YEARS AND OLDER EAT**
two servings of fruit and 5.5 servings of vegetables per day

**WHAT IS A SERVING?**

» ½ cup of green or orange vegetables,

» ½ cup cooked beans/lentils/chick peas,

» One cup of green leafy vegetables

» One medium size potato.

» One medium size banana, apple, pear or orange

» Two small fruits like kiwi, plums and mandarins.

Life expectancy would grow in leaps and bounds if vegetables smelled as good as bacon

*Doug Larson*

In May 2012, the Australian Bureau of Statistics released a report looking at the fruit and vegetable eating habits of Australian children and adults. Here is the reality:

**57%**
of children aged 5 - 7 years old

**32%**
of children aged 8 - 11 years

**5%**
of people aged 12 - 18 years and

**6%**
of people 19 years and older

**EAT THE RECOMMENDED AMOUNT OF FRUITS AND VEGETABLES**

## SETTING THE EXAMPLE

### So how can we get our children to eat more fruits and vegetables?

I am sure you have noticed it doesn't work particularly well to tell them, even when you explain why. Children, as we all very well know, do as we do, not as we say. So if you enjoy chips and biscuits, that is what they will want to eat as well. What may work better is for the whole family to agree that everyone enjoys a piece of fruit or a carrot before munching on a bit of the special stuff.

Like many families, we used to enjoy having lovely picnics at the park or at the beach when our kids were little. We would bring the picnic blanket and purchase some prawns, a ripe avocado, cherry tomatoes, some lovely sourdough bread and some vegemite. What a treat! We used to tell the kids that the prawns were yucky, fishy and full of prawn brains and prawn poo that would make their fingers smell. We would try to convince them that they should eat the bread with avocado and tomatoes or the vegemite, and leave the yucky, smelly prawns to the parents. It worked for a while. A very short while!

**Professor Albert Mehrabian's communication model** explains the impact of our verbal communication: 7% comes from the words we use, 38% comes from our tone of voice, our pitch, speed and inflection, and, believe it or not, a whopping 55% of what is understood is nonverbal – the way we stand, use our hands and our facial expressions.

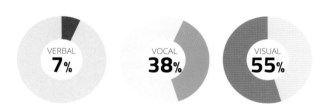

Professor Albert Mehrabian's communication model

Our kids picked up on the prawn trick pretty quickly. They observed us savouring and enjoying the prawns; they could see from our happy, smiling faces that this was a special treat, and although they heard our words, they understood what we were actually saying and wanted some too. Good for them! We still have this special picnic routine. Now we just buy more prawns.

# NON-VERBAL COMMUNICATION

Non-verbal communication about food is everywhere. Think of the message you convey when you come home tired from work and plop yourself down in front of the TV with a beer and a bag of chips. How about after a busy day of shopping when you throw yourself onto the couch with your feet up, enjoying a cup of tea and a biscuit? The kids understand: *'Aha, this is what you do when you want to relax'.* Similarly, what message are you giving your children when you congratulate their efforts for listening well at their swimming lessons with ice cream or lollies?

Food is for sustenance – for growing, for health, for the best function of our brains and bodies – and for this reason, our food choices should be based on this fact. Once our children accept this, we will have a lot less emotional eating, fighting at dinner time and dependence on certain foods.

As already mentioned, start with making better choices for yourself and show your kids that you are enjoying your selection. It is your enjoyment that they will pick up on. Pile your plate high with healthy foods: fruits, vegetables, protein and whatever you want your children to eat. Make sure they see you eat it. Smile, savour and enjoy what is on your plate. Take the time to actually taste it and to feel the different textures in your mouth. Visualise the amazing benefits this particular food has to your health and wellbeing; how your body will replenish, heal and function from this nourishing delight. Be open, relaxed and smiling when you dish up the family meal. Expect everyone to love your creation and don't worry if they don't. Whenever possible, make meal times family time where everyone comes together to connect, interact and chat about his or her day. Be prepared to tell your own funny tale and ask open-ended questions of everyone, showing a keen interest in their answers. You want to focus on creating healthy associations with food; the life-giving essence that it really is.

I perfectly understand how difficult it can be, but it is important not to argue about food. Children know from a very young age that you can't make them eat, and you don't want to get caught in an emotional struggle you will never win by trying to negotiate, reason, beg or threaten your child to eat their food. Try as best you can to stay calm and neutral and ignore their tantrums. Being hungry is motivating. It is much healthier for a child to go hungry for a few hours or skip a meal — this will not hurt them! — rather than create and maintain disruptive habits which will hurt their health for a lifetime. Remember that you are, at the end of the day, responsible for what, when and where your child eats and she will only eat chicken nuggets, hot dogs and unhealthy foods if they are available.

Another thing to keep in mind is that babies, and toddlers in particular, are hardwired to enjoy sweet things and that their taste buds take time to mature to other tastes. You may have to be prepared to serve a new food maybe twenty times before it gets accepted as something suitable for eating. Don't conclude that just because your child does not eat the vegetable you have served her (and has very possibly thrown it on the floor), that she does not like it. Not yet, anyway. She is just testing it out.

# BRAIN FUNCTION

I think a part of parents' fear around food and eating comes from the horrible pictures and tales of people suffering severe malnutrition that we have all experienced through TV, books, newspapers or our elders' wartime horror stories. We know starvation is devastating for physical, mental and emotional health. Interestingly though, malnutrition is not just a question of low calorie intake. A high calorie diet of junk food also causes malnutrition and has a significant impact not just on the body, but just as importantly, on the brain.

In this day and age, we spend millions on teacher's aides, tutoring and home-based computer learning programs. We spend hours and hours coaching and coaxing, motivating and threatening, wanting our children to succeed at learning and performing at school. And sometimes, it is like pushing big rocks up a mountain! Hard work, slow going and not very rewarding. If we took a holistic view on health and brain function, though, we would get results much more easily. Studies have shown that a diet high in bad fats and calories actually decreases our cognitive function (34, 37). This means that if we eat lots of junk food, it has a damaging effect on our brain function, making it harder to think, concentrate and learn. Restricting caloric intake appears to improve the function of the brain (38). Research has also shown that the fatter the child is, the harder he or she finds learning at school.

The BMI is inversely related to academic, mathematic and reading achievement (39). This doesn't mean that your overweight child is not bright! It just means that if we look at the statistics over many children, being on the bigger side is definitely not good for school performance.

It is tempting to draw the conclusion that fatty foods are the cause of all our troubles and the solution lies in choosing items at the supermarket which carry the 'Healthy Tick' for low fat content. This is not what I am trying to say, not at all! What I am talking about has more to do with the quality of the nutrients in the food we are eating. Fatty, processed foods are not providing your child with optimal building blocks for growth and development. However, often the 'low fat' versions are not great choices either. If you were to compare the ingredients lists of two similar products, one normal and one low-fat, what you will see is that the ingredients list on the low-fat version is often much longer. The reason for this is that the fat contributes a lot of flavour to food, and if we remove it, the food tastes 'blah'. So to make it palatable, the food manufacturers add sugars, flavourings and flavour enhancers, many of which are artificial. More on this in just a moment.

*Fatty, processed foods are not providing your child with optimal building blocks for growth and development. However, often the 'low fat' versions are not great choices either.*

## SPECIAL TREATS AND TIPS

### We all love special treats.

They definitely have their place - to celebrate, to encourage and to make us feel better. Treats don't have to be food, though. Special time together or a new toy can work just as well. Some ideas include reading your child's favourite book together, going for a walk to the park, inviting a friend over for a sleep-over or building a Lego tower together. You can choose healthier treats like a punnet of blueberries, a box of sultanas, dried mango, frozen banana, watermelon or orange segments, and then there are icy poles made of frozen pureed fruit. Dip these in plain chocolate and they are divine!

Here are some tips which I have found helpful over the years, both with my own family and when advising parents in my practice about helping kids to eat (and sustain) a balanced diet with more fruit and vegetables:

# HEALTHY EATING TIPS

» **Serve small, well-presented portions.** Try not to overwhelm, and when it looks that good on the plate, it will probably taste good, too!

» **Serve vegetables raw, cut into interesting, easy-to-handle shapes.** You can use the peeler to make carrot, cucumber and apple shavings, or cut into the sides of carrots and cucumbers to make flowers or shapes when sliced.

» **Serve raw veggies as an appetiser while dinner is cooking when everyone is really hungry.** Sticks of carrots, celery, cucumber, capsicum, raw beans, snow peas or peas are easy to nibble on. Frozen corn or peas are delicious to crunch on, too.

» **A whole piece of fruit can be too much to handle.** Cut it into bite sizes or invest in a slinky-cutter. String the pieces onto toothpicks, skewers or even a piece of string just for fun.

» **Have fruit and vegetables already cut up** in a container in the fridge ready to feast on.

» **If your child has no allergies to nuts, they are also great.** They are filling and an excellent source of protein and healthy fats to enjoy any time.

» **Have hardboiled eggs** ready in the fridge for a quick protein-rich snack.

» **Have the fruit and vegetables already cut up** in a small plastic container or sealed bag to put in the school or sports bag.

» **Enjoy the art of creating a lovely meal together as a family.** Let your children help prepare the food – under appropriate supervision, of course – and include them in the washing, peeling, cutting and cooking.

» **Make collages and creatures of the fruit and vegetables,** dress the plate as a smiley face, use toothpicks and skewers to make a person or an animal. Be creative!

» **Chop or grind nuts** and drizzle them along with different seeds onto salads, cereals, porridge and desserts.

» **Have delicious and healthy dips** such as hummus or mashed avocado to dip vegetable sticks into.

» **Have nut spreads** available for healthy snacks (almond, brazil, macadamia, cashew or a mixture). Spread on fruit slices, vegetables and crackers.

» **Have fun together growing vegetables in your garden or in pots.** Tomatoes, peas, carrots, snow peas, beans, lettuce and beetroot are a good place to start. Nothing tastes as good as freshly picked, home grown veggies.

» **Make soups.** Vegetables taste delicious both chunky in a broth or blended nice and smooth.

» **Make juices.** You can 'hide' a carrot, celery, beetroot, spinach or kale in the apple and orange juice that way.

» **Puree** zucchini, carrots, sweet potato and pumpkin and put it in everything you make, including bolognaise, meat patties, mashed potatoes, muffins and cakes.

» **Shop with your kids** and let them choose which fruits, vegetable and unprocessed meats they prefer during the week.

» **Make up cute names for vegetables:** snow trees for cauliflower and superman food for spinach.

» **Have a family rule** of having to try one bite of everything on the plate before you say 'No thank you'.

# SUGAR

*Sugar, the white, sweet, yummy stuff added to low fat foods, is really just fat in a different form.*

Your liver converts the glucose and fructose – the compounds which make up table sugar – straight into fat (so really, you didn't gain much by avoiding the fat in the first place with your low-fat choice). The sugar added to our foods, and low-fat foods in particular, is often not labelled as 'sugar'. The manufacturers are not that silly. They use many different types of sweetening products, most of which will appear as names unbeknown to you. This means they don't have to list sugar as the first and main ingredient, but can 'hide' the sugar content behind other ingredients, as they are supposedly present in larger quantities. A quick Internet search shows seventy different names for sugar, and that doesn't even include any artificial sweeteners! Galactose, fruit juice concentrate, ethyl maltol, corn syrup solids, maltodextrin and high fructose corn syrup are just a few of the hidden sweeteners. So seriously, my heartfelt advice, if you want a treat, go the full hog – full-cream, full-fat, and enjoy the beautiful taste, in moderation of course! At least it is *real food.*

The World Health Organisation (WHO) recommends that we consume less than 25 grams of sugar per day. One teaspoon is four grams of sugar, so that means that we should eat less than six teaspoons of sugar per day. The American Heart Association (40) reports that the average sugar consumption across all ages in 2001-2004 was 22.2 teaspoons per day. Children fourteen to eighteen years old had the highest consumption, at 34.3 teaspoons per day. Before you sit back and think *'That's America'*, let me gently break the facts to you.

The numbers are actually worse for Australia. Despite research showing that the Australian sugar consumption actually decreased almost 9% from 2004 to 2012 (41), we still consume on average across all ages, 42 kilos of sugar per year per person. That is 115 grams of sugar per capita per day - 28 teaspoons of sugar! Think about it... This means that, on average, 25% of our recommended daily calorie intake comes from added sugar.

When you look at this list of sugar content, it becomes apparent why it adds up so quickly:

- Coke 350 ml - **9 teaspoons**
- Apple juice 350 ml - **10 teaspoons**
- Orange juice 350 ml - **8 teaspoons**
- Fruit yogurt one cup - **7 teaspoons**
- Muesli with dried fruit 50g - **3 teaspoons**
- Nutri-Grain 50g - **4 teaspoons**
- Two slices of white bread - **1 teaspoon** (that's without anything added!)

So what's wrong with sugar, apart from causing obesity, heart trouble, diabetes, cancer and so on? Several books have been written on this topic and I will let you read those to form your own opinion. My perspective as a Chiropractor working with children has made me question the sugar in our foods. My main concern is the challenges it appears to cause in the function of children's brains with regards to learning, attention and behaviour.

My husband and I tried to be less strict with our children's diets when we were away on holidays. Let's be realistic; even as adults we want to let down our hair and enjoy a special treat or two in the shape a glass of wine and a few biscuits with cheese at sundown. So on one particular camping trip, we let our kids choose the breakfast cereal and chips they were dying to try. This experiment lasted just this one camping trip, as it took approximately five minutes from breakfast consumption to total tent destruction, with both kids bouncing and climbing the inside of the tent after enjoying their 'Loop-de-Loops' and 'Psycho-pops'. Sorry, there are limits to the madness we can endure.

Backing this opinion up with research is somewhat challenging because most studies conclude there is no such link between sugar consumption in children and difficulties learning, sustaining attention or behaviour. However, given the vested interest in this outcome from the sugar industry, it may be a bit like it used to be trying to find studies linking smoking and lung cancer.

There are plenty of studies however, which demonstrate the effects of sugar on children diagnosed with ADHD. One study showed that the total amount of sugar eaten relative to healthy foods and the ratio between carbohydrates and protein eaten were all factors influencing play behaviour. The more sugar and carbohydrates consumed, the more destructive, aggressive and restless behaviour the kids displayed (42). Another study showed that sugar consumption appeared to interfere with the way the neuro-chemicals work in the brain (43) and it also messes with ADHD children's already troubled sleep patterns, further increasing challenging behaviour (44).

In a study on nearly 2,000 Australian children, researchers found that children eating a 'Western' style diet were more likely to have a diagnosis of ADHD compared to children who had a more 'healthy diet'. The Western diet was described as being full of red meat, sugar, fats and processed foods, and low in whole grains, fresh fruits, and vegetables (45). And yet another study showed that children who regularly eat 'junk food' at age four were more likely to be diagnosed with ADHD at age seven (46).

'So what's wrong with sugar, apart from causing obesity, heart trouble, diabetes and cancer?'

# ARTIFICIAL ADDITIVES

*So avoiding or minimising refined sugars in children's diets, whether they are diagnosed with ADHD or not, is greatly beneficial. However, be aware that replacing the refined sugar with artificial sugars is actually worse.*

There are many artificial sweeteners on the market: saccharin, aspartame (Nutra sweet), sorbitol, sucralose, xylitol and mannitol, to name a few, all celebrated for being guilt-free because they have no calories and don't cause dental problems. However, they can have serious detrimental health effects, such as causing cancer and problems with neurotransmitter levels in the brain (47, 48). Moreover, recent evidence suggests that these substances can confuse our body's ability to feel full and satisfied, sweet-wise. This can cause us to crave more sweets and overeat, leading to metabolic syndrome (high blood pressure, elevated triglycerides, low levels of good cholesterol, high fasting blood sugar and large waists), obesity and cardiovascular disease (49, 50), as well as diabetes (51).

Artificial sweeteners are not the only artificial chemicals we are exposed to through our food. Basically, anything we purchase in a packet has additives added to it in some way. Food producers add additives to make their products look more appetising, taste better, last longer and store better.

Many additives are artificial, meaning they are chemical compounds which have been produced in a laboratory. Regardless of their source, additives can be a problem. Additives have been linked to cancer, gut irritation, high blood pressure and sleep disturbances, as well as learning and behaviour difficulties. It is thought that the chemicals can irritate brain and nervous system function by mimicking other neurotransmitters.

Food additives are a huge business. There are currently 3000 additives approved for food use by the US Food and Drug Administration (FDA) (52), and these are often by-products from the manufacturing of something else. It is estimated that Australian kids eat up to five kilos of additives per year, many of them already banned in Europe and USA (53). The consumption is similar in America, where it is estimated that every individual eats 13-15 grams of additives per day (54).

The problem with food additives is that the body doesn't recognise the chemicals and can't use them for anything. Hence, these ingredients can irritate the body and brain and may cause a state of inflammation in the gut, disturb our sleep and cause behaviour problems.

Dr. Ben Feingold, a paediatrician and allergist in America, pioneered the idea that additives can interfere with brain function more than forty years ago. He devised a diet which eliminates synthetic colouring, artificial flavours, preservatives, salicylates (a substance found in many plant foods), nitrites, sulphites and MSG, and found it to be extremely successful with regards to children's behaviour, concentration and learning, as well as health problems (55). The community, the medical profession and the governments still don't agree whether additives are an issue or not. Considering the amount of money involved, I suppose that is no surprise!

**Additives to look out for:**

- anti-caking agents
- stabilisers
- emulsifiers (to avoid fat clotting)
- bulking agents
- anti-oxidants
- humectants (to keep foods moist)
- thickeners
- bleaching agents
- flavouring
- colouring
- preservatives

Even if you make a conscious decision to try to decrease your family's consumption of additives, it can be really hard to avoid them. Firstly because of the confusing numbers: Baking powder and baking soda are often listed as numbers (eg, E500), as are spices like turmeric (E100) and Vitamin C (E300-305). These are obviously fine to eat as long as they're natural. Also, additives do not have to be listed on the ingredients list if they are present under a certain level, which means you can't actually trust the ingredients list. If the additives were added to the ingredients used, but not by the manufacturer themselves, they don't have to be listed.

**Generally, the E-numbers are categorised like this:**

- E100+: Colours
- E200+: Preservatives
- E300+: Antioxidants
- E400+: Miscellaneous

## Here are a few 'heads-up' about additives:

### MSG (MONOSODIUM GLUTAMATE)

You will remember that there was a revolt against this being added to our food many years back. As a result, food producers stopped adding MSG. Hooray!! However, they did start adding gelatin, calcium caseinate, hydrolized vegetable protein, textured protein, monopotassium glutamate, hydrolized plant protein, yeast extract, glutamate, autolyzed plant protein, glutamic acid, sodium caseinate, whey protein and soy sauce. These are all MSG by another name! (56). MSG has been linked to many adverse health effects, such as behavioural and learning problems in children, sleep disturbances, anger, asthma, skin rashes, migraines, obesity and brain tumours. Other brain disorders such as Parkinsons and Alzheimers have also been associated with MSG exposure, as have hormonal and endocrine health problems (57).

**MSG numbers to look out for:**

- E620 Glutamic acid
- E621 Monosodium glutamate
- E622 Monopotassium glutamate
- E623 Calcium diglutamate
- E624 Monoammonium glutamate
- E625 Magnesium diglutamate

### COLOURINGS

The artificial colourings in our foodstuffs here in Australia are supposed to be safe for humans to ingest as they have been assessed and regulated by Food Standards Australia and New Zealand (FSANZ). However, studies are showing that colours such as tartrazine (E102), allura red (E129), sunset yellow (FCF110), and ponceau 4R (E124) have a number of health risks, such as cancers, allergic reactions and hyperactivity in children (58-60). Annato (E160b), which is a natural yellow colouring made from seeds of the Achiote tree, has been linked to similar health risks (61). Cochineal (E120), a natural dye made from crushed beetles, is suspected of embryo toxicity and is linked to hyperactivity in children (62).

# PRESERVATIVES

*With regards to preservatives, there are some that are worse than others.*

**Sodium nitrate and nitrite (E249 – 252) are common preservatives used in processed meats such as bacon, sausages and deli meats.  The World Health Organisation (WHO) has warned for at least 40 years now that sodium nitrate and nitrite are 'probably carcinogenic to humans'.  Only now in 2015 is the warning explicit: Processed meats cause cancer (63).**

Benzoates (E210-213), which are often found in fruit drinks, have been linked to cancer and hyperactivity in children.  Sulphites (E220 - 225 and 228), common in wine and dried fruits, have been shown to cause intolerance symptoms such as asthma, headaches, skin rashes, abdominal cramping and diarrhoea (64).

A study in Lancet (65) looked at the possible connection between food additives and hyperactive behaviour in three year olds and eight to nine year olds.  153 three year olds and 144 eight to nine year olds were given drinks with sodium benzoate (a food preservative), a drink with artificial colours or a placebo.  The study found that both colour and preservatives caused increased hyperactivity in both age groups.  As a result, certain colours and preservatives were banned in UK in 2009, but not yet in the USA or Australia.

When research into additives takes place, most studies look at the effect of one additive at a time.  Unfortunately this is not how it works in real life.  When we eat foods with artificial ingredients we generally have a combination of quite a few in just one sitting.  It is important to realise that the combined effect of different additives is much more potent on the brain and body than one plus one, potentially causing a manifold increase in the reaction (66).

Not every child will react to additives, nor will all kids with ADHD, which is possibly why it can be argued that the additives are safe to consume.  Research suggests that a child's genetic predisposition and possible underlying state of inflammation determines the degree of reaction (67).  From a child's health perspective, though, whether she reacts or not, it is probably best to avoid or minimise additives where possible.

*So you really have to think before you buy, as well as using a good measure of common sense.  If a product can last a long time and still be soft and delicious, there is probably a reason, and it is not a good one.  A good rule of thumb is the shorter the list of ingredients, the better! Also, stick to the periphery of the supermarket where the fresh food is, or better still, shop at your local farmer's market.*

# EPIGENETICS

*We are born with a ton of genes in the DNA of our cells. The genes are our potential.*

We are born with many, many more genes than we will ever be able to express. Some genes are non-negotiable and will be expressed no matter what, right from the word go. For example, there are genes that determine whether we are born as a human rather than a koala or a flea, and whether we are a boy or a girl. Then we have genes that are not expressed straight away, but will be when the time is right. Will you grow bald or not? We have a huge number of genes that are just sitting there and will be turned on or not depending on what happens in our lives. Take for example the gene for height. You have a certain potential to grow to a particular height depending on the genes you have inherited from your parents, grandparents, great grandparents and so on. However, if you are exposed to famine, starvation and malnutrition early in your life, you may never reach the genetic potential you are born with. Or you may carry the gene for a certain type of cancer; the gene sits in your cells, but the cancer would never develop if the gene does not get read. It is only a potential. This gene may or may not ever be expressed, depending on the experiences you have in your life, the choices you make, the places you live and the toxins and stresses you are exposed to.

This is the age-old nature versus nurture discussion, except it is not just talk anymore. We know now through science that we develop from both and that they are equally important. The science of epigenetics is concerned with how cells read their genes, how the genes are turned on or off depending on our external environment and then which genes are expressed, based on that. Epigenetics gives us back our power to have some control over our potential for health rather than being passive prisoners of our genes. The choices we make in our lives affect our health and wellbeing now, in the future and for future generations.

# OUR TWO BRAINS

**So how does what we eat affect our brain function? I was initially taken back a bit when our new Naturopath suggested we make some changes to Signe's diet to help her learn and concentrate. I felt that we as a family were very aware of our diet, making most of our foods from scratch, avoiding toxins, junk food and artificial anything. I was, at that time, not aware how important the gut function is for brain function. If the gut is not working at optimum, it is not able to digest the 'healthy' food properly, which has serious implications not just for the body, but also the brain.**

*"All diseases begin in the gut"*
~ Hippocrates

## Let me explain.

Humans are actually the proud owners of two separate, but connected brains. We have the brain in our head, which receives the credit for being in charge of everything. Then we have the brain of the gut, called the Enteric Nervous System (ENS), which, like the "main brain", sends and receives messages, and has memories and emotions. The ENS can quite happily function without any input from above, digesting food, absorbing nutrients and expelling the leftovers, all the while feeling and monitoring what is going on (68).

Both brains are created from identical tissue during foetal development and are connected by nerves. We generally think that the brain controls the function of all the organs in our body by sending messages about what needs to get done. Interestingly, in the case of our ENS, there is 90% more information going from the gut to the brain than the other way. The ENS gets the job done and keeps the big brain informed at a subconscious level.

There are one hundred million nerve cells in our ENS, which is actually more nerve cells than in the spinal cord, and these cells are embedded in the gut wall from the oesophagus to the rectum. It is these nerve cells which are responsible for all the communication.

Neurotransmitters are the chemicals that nerves use to communicate. Many of the neurotransmitters used by the brain are also found in the gut tissues. For example, 95% of our body's levels of serotonin – a neurotransmitter associated with depression – are found in the gut. 50% of the body's levels of dopamine are also found in the gut. Dopamine is a neurotransmitter related to brain function, learning and feel-good behaviour, and is also thought to be involved in the symptoms associated with ADHD.

The gut brain very much influences our brain upstairs. Excitement, fear, sadness, stress and depression are all felt in the gut and relayed up north.

## Let's have a closer look at the gut.

# YOUR GUT

Our digestive system starts with the mouth and ends with the anus. The act of chewing our food and mixing it with saliva starts the process of breaking down our food into useful, nutrient-rich, energy-producing molecules such as proteins, carbohydrates and fats, which our bodies then use for energy, growing and cell renewal. Chewing allows us to manageably and comfortably propel our food, now chewed to liquid pulp, through our oesophagus to the stomach, where the pulp gets treated to a serious acid bath. The pulp is gently sloshed around the stomach for hours, getting exposed to and broken down by acids and enzymes. When the food pulp is broken down to small enough pieces it gets released into the small intestine. Here the *chyme*, as the food is now called, continues to be broken down by enzymes from the small intestine, the pancreas, the liver and the gall bladder, with some help from bacteria. The resultant amino acids, simple sugars, broken-down fats, vitamins and salts, as well as minerals and water, get absorbed through the cell wall of the small intestine into our blood stream. From here the nutrients go to the liver for cleaning and then on to all our cells to keep us alive.

The permeability of the small intestine cell wall controls what can get through the walls into the blood stream. Unabsorbed material, including waste and toxins, get sent further along the system to be dealt with and eventually eliminated from the body. The large intestine does the final absorption of nutrients and water, leaving indigestible food bits, dead cells from the rest of the digestive system and bacteria to get stored in the rectum and pooped out at a later time.

To ensure that our gut digests our food properly, we rely on a bit of help from our friends. All 100 trillion them! We have about 500 species of indigenous, friendly bacteria living in our gut, helping us digest our foods, making vitamins and hormones, training our immune system and keeping unhealthy bacteria at bay. Some of them we know quite well, like *Lactobacillus* and *Bifidobacteria*, as these are the ones we can buy in bottles at the health food store as probiotics. Some lesser known ones are *Propionobacteria*, *Enterococci* and some healthy, helpful strains of (believe it or not!) *E. Coli* (69).

We are born with a basically sterile gut. The split second we are exposed to real life out of mum's protective womb, our little friends move in. If a baby is born vaginally, she will be inoculated with mum's vaginal (many strains of the Lactobacteria) and gut bacteria as she passes through the birth canal (70), and the baby's gut flora will be well established within the first month. If the baby is born by caesarean, the first exposure to bacteria will be from the skin of the mother, doctors and nurses, the hospital equipment and the air, and this is not where you find the beneficial gut bacteria (71). It takes more than six months to establish a better gut flora in these babies, making them more prone to digestive issues, immune dysfunction, asthma, eczema and allergies (69).

The gut bacteria take up residence along the cell walls in our gut. They make a physical barrier for the gut cells to protect them against toxins, parasites, undigested food and other harmful bacteria, as well as providing the gut cells with nutrients. As they settle in, they take up precious real estate and fight for the available sustenance, making it difficult for other bacteria and pathogens to move in and take hold. They excrete anti-bacterial, anti-fungal and anti-viral compounds and neutralise many toxins and cancer-causing agents (69).

The establishment of a healthy mix of gut flora from early on is very important. The initial bacteria teach the immune system that they are the good guys and that the immune system should attack and destroy other bacteria so that they cannot colonise the gut. This is a wonderful way to keep a healthy gut healthy. However, it can make it very difficult to change an existing non-optimal gut flora for the better.

*Breastfeeding is one of the most important factors in establishing the early healthy mix of bacteria (72).*

It improves the baby's overall immune function (73), providing protection against a wide range of infections while he is feeding, as well as decreasing the risk of Sudden Infant Death Syndrome (SIDS), leukaemia, lymphoma, allergies and obesity much later in life (74, 75). Breastfeeding has also been shown to increase the baby's cognitive performance (76), IQ and educational levels (77).

You may have heard that 70-80% of your immune response comes from your gut. The whole intestinal tract is jam-packed with tissues that produce the different kinds of white blood cells and chemicals which help the body disarm invading bacteria, parasites, viruses and toxins. The healthy gut bacteria communicate with these tissues to teach them the difference between the good guys, which are welcome in the body and can be left alone, and the bad guys, which may be a danger to the body and need to be destroyed – not just in the gut, but anywhere in the body. All molecules that enter our bodies through our mouths, our airways or our skin need to be assessed for danger. Is this an antigen - a foreign particle of danger to the body which the immune system needs to attack, destroy and make antibodies against for future reference? Or is it ultimately ok? For example, is cat hair, gluten, a splinter or pollen a danger that needs to be addressed, or just a normal part of life? If the immune system learns to recognise these as foreign it will establish a war whenever exposed and respond with inflammation, swelling and discomfort as a result.

When our gut is healthy, we have a predominance of the *'indigenous friendly'* bacteria as we have just discussed. However, even then about 15% of our gut flora consists of *'opportunistic flora'*, which do not support our health and function. Bacteria like *Staphylococci*, *Streptococci*, *Clostridia* and *Enterobacteria*, as well as fungi, parasites and viruses are kept in tight check by our friendly bacteria.

If the bacterial composition in your gut gets out of balance it can lead to *'Gut Dysbiosis'*. This means there is an unhealthy balance between the good guys and the bad guys in your gut, with the bad guys taking over. Since the bad guys don't help you break down your food or help the immune system to do its job, it is not a good place to be. The growth of the unhealthy bacteria damages the protective barrier of the gut wall, exposing it to toxins, partly digested food, fungi, viruses, parasites and bacteria and promotes inflammation of the gut cells. This will damage the gut wall cells and change the permeability of the gut lining. Normally the cells in the gut wall are nice and close together, only allowing molecules of a certain size through. A *'Leaky Gut'*, however, means the cells are damaged and prised apart by certain types of bad bacteria, allowing larger, partly digested food bits to pass through the cell wall and into the bloodstream. The body's immune system does not recognise these larger molecules and will attack them as foreign. This can lead to inflammation in the whole body, food allergies and intolerances, malabsorption and nutritional deficiencies. It has also been linked to autism, ADHD, dyspraxia, dyslexia, behavioural problems, asthma, allergies, eczema, depression, bipolar disorder, obsessive compulsive disorder and schizophrenia (69).

An example of what may happen with a Leaky Gut is when proteins from milk and wheat are only partly digested and broken down. These larger molecules, which are now capable of entering the bloodstream are very similar in structure to the proteins in morphine/opium/cocaine, and can cause some serious problems in the body. They are also able to cross the blood-brain barrier and attach to the receptors in the brain (69), causing the person to feel spaced out and unable to concentrate, and being 'addicted' to milk and wheat products.

# POSSIBLE CAUSES OF GUT DYSBIOSIS AND LEAKY GUT

Many things affect the health of our gut flora, and thereby our health, such as chronic stress, illness and medication. Some examples include:

- **The most obvious danger to the health of our friendly bacteria is antibiotics.** On average, by the time a child is five years old, she will have been exposed to 2.3 lots of antibiotics. 69% of all children have had antibiotics by the time they are two years old (78). Unfortunately, most of these prescriptions are unnecessary, given for viral infections such as sore throats, common colds, ear infections (*otitis media*), bronchitis and sinus infections (79). Antibiotics do not kill viruses, but they do kill the bacteria, including the healthy, helpful ones in our guts.

- **Prescription antibiotics are not our only exposure.** Antibiotics are used extensively in farming; farm animals and poultry often live in very close quarters and antibiotics are frequently used to prevent or stop outbreaks of disease. Antibiotics are also used to fatten up livestock (80). As a result, their meat, milk and eggs will contain antibiotics. Farmed fish are frequently given antibiotics, and fruit and vegetables are sprayed with them for disease control. Unnecessary use of antibiotics has been blamed for the increase in the number of dangerous antibiotic-resistant bacteria in our community and has also been shown to be associated with childhood obesity (78).

- **Other medications can interfere with our gut flora as well,** especially if they are taken over a period of time. 'Over the counter' painkillers and anti-inflammatories, heartburn medication, steroids for asthma and the contraceptive pill all cause significant damage to the indigenous gut flora (69).

- **Exposure to toxins of all kinds,** including dental amalgams, medications with mercury, lead paint, plastics, herbicides, pesticides, insecticides, PCBs and fertilisers are well known to be damaging to our gut flora (69).

- **Different illnesses will challenge the gut flora:** diarrhoea, both bacterial and viral, endocrine disorders, diabetes, auto-immune diseases and morning sickness (69).

- **Our diet plays a major role in our gut health,** as the gut flora responds to what we feed it. As mentioned, breastfeeding promotes the health of our gut flora. Baby's first foods do as well. Does rice cereal provide your child with the optimum mix of amino acids, vitamins, carbohydrates, minerals and fatty acids needed for growth, development, healing and gut health? Or would it be more beneficial nutritionally to start with avocado, pear, steamed zucchini and pumpkin? We all need a combination of lots of different foods to provide us with all the nutrients we need, no matter what our age. Too often we, and even more so, our children, eat the same type of foods most of the time. Weetabix with milk for breakfast, maybe with a slice of toast, and then biscuits, crackers and maybe an apple for morning tea. Then we eat a sandwich for lunch, chips or cake after school and pasta (hopefully with some meat and veggies) for dinner, with ice cream for dessert. Wheat and dairy, dairy and wheat! The average family cooks and eats the same nine dishes over and over again.

- **Our soils are depleted of nutrients,** so our food contains less vitamins and minerals than in years gone past.

- **Genetic modification and chemical spraying** of our crops are ever-expanding problems; implicated not only in gut but many other health issues as well.

- **Emotional stress** diverts our blood supply from our digestive tract to the heart, lungs and major muscles to prepare us to either fight or flee. For a short time, this is no big deal. However, if we are living in this state for an extended time, the gut does not receive the essential blood supply and with it, the oxygen and nutrients it needs. This is not an optimal state for our friendly bacteria. They suffer and the bad guys take over.

- **Cleanliness** - Believe it or not, but being too clean is a big problem. We live in a world of bacteria. We are totally surrounded by them: they are in the air, in our water, in our beds, on the kitchen counter and the school floor. They live on us and in us: on our skin, on our hands, in our noses, throat and lungs. They are everywhere. Some bacteria are bad guys; they cause colds, flus, food poisoning and worse. Most of the bacteria around us though are just there. They don't actually do us any harm. As we have just described about the gut, some bacteria are absolutely essential for our survival.

## Let me explain

During my early years here in Australia.... actually, this is a lie – even now – I am petrified of snakes. They are scary, scaly, slimy and sure to attack and kill my family and me just by being in the same state. A few years back, I was walking back from the beach with my children when I saw a HUGE snake crossing the road and making its way into our front garden. I absolutely freaked, and ran screaming, kids in tow, around the house to get in the back door. When safely in the house, I slammed the door as fast as I could and locked it! Pheww, safe! Visualising all the ways the snake could enter the house – the bathroom drain, the kitchen exhaust, under the garage door and through the keyhole, I rang the police, the fire department, the dog rescue and RSPCA. I finally got through to a gentleman who was willing to listen to me screaming and hyper-ventilating about the immense danger my family was in. He had me describe the six meter (at least!) monster, and when I finally shut up to breathe he calmly explained to me how it worked. It sounded like it was a diamond python, which is totally harmless unless you try to hit it on the head with a spade. The diamond python is a big snake that eats lots of food and needs a big territory. It fights off smaller, nastier, aggressive and poisonous snakes. So he advised that I celebrate that I had such a good snake in my front yard as it was very unlikely I would have any dangerous snakes anywhere nearby. All afternoon my family and I played traffic police as we stopped cars to let the snake pass safely as it repeatedly crossed the road to pay a visit to our equally fortunate neighbours.

This is similar to how the harmless bacteria work in your body; they keep the nasty ones at bay. In a 2015 study in the British Medical Journal, researchers compared the health of children in clean and not-so-clean households. They found children who lived in houses that were regularly cleaned with bleach (which kills ALL the bacteria, both the good and bad) were much sicker than the kids that lived in less germo-phobic homes. The bleach kids had 18% greater risk of any type of infection, 20% higher risk of flu and 35% higher risk of recurrent tonsillitis (81).

# FOOD ALLERGIES AND INTOLERANCES

Looking at the list on the previous pages, it is apparent why the bacteria in our guts don't thrive as they should, causing so many kids and adults to suffer with gut dysbiosis, leaky gut and poor nutrient absorption, learning difficulties, attention problems and behavioural dysfunction.

I mentioned earlier that a Leaky Gut can cause food allergies and intolerances. There is a lot of confusion as to what that means and what the differences are. A classic description of a food allergy is the immediate reaction experienced after eating even the tiniest amount of whatever you may be allergic to, for example peanuts, eggs, soy beans, milk, tree nuts, seafood or shellfish. This reaction happens in the immune system. Due to a previous exposure, the immune system has made antibodies which immediately recognize the allergen (the protein in the food you are allergic to) as toxic and goes on the attack. Histamine and other chemicals are released in the body, causing inflammation. The allergic response can be dizziness, vomiting, diarrhoea, itching, a rash or swelling, and may be so serious it can lead to anaphylactic shock. An allergy like this can be diagnosed by your medical doctor by doing a skin prick test or a blood test. According to the NSW Government Food Authority, one in twenty children suffers with food allergies.

Food intolerance is not the same as a food allergy. Food intolerance is an inability of the gut to properly digest a particular food and the reaction that this causes in the body, so the immune system is not involved in the same way. Food intolerance is dose dependent – the more you eat, the worse the symptoms. Often the reaction takes a while to occur (up to 24 hours sometimes), so you may not even be aware that your body is reacting to something you have eaten. The discomfort may hang around for many hours after eating the offending food, and it is also very common to be intolerant to many different foods, so the effects get really hard to measure. The NSW Government Food Authority estimates that one in four people suffers with food intolerances.

Please be aware that the distinction between food allergies and intolerances is not quite as simple as I have suggested here. Food allergies can be dose-dependent and have delayed onset, and the chemical reaction of food intolerance may be immediate and severe.

**Some common symptoms associated with food intolerances include the following:**

- headaches
- stomach aches
- flatulence
- dark circles around the eyes
- bedwetting
- irritable bowel
- chronic fatigue
- immune dysfunction such as eczema
- rhinitis (runny nose)
- asthma and ear infections
- behaviour changes like lack of concentration
- fidgetiness and mood changes
- Autistic Spectrum Disorders
- ADHD
- schizophrenia
- depression
- psychosis
- auto-immune disorders

(54, 69)

The most common "foods" that kids with ADHD are intolerant to are food additives and colouring, sugar, dairy products (casein and lactose), wheat (gluten), corn, yeast, soy, citrus, eggs, chocolate, nuts and tomatoes (54).

# Gluten and dairy

As already noted, wheat and dairy are common offenders in both allergy and intolerance. I want to point out a couple of important distinctions:

- **Gluten is a protein present in grains - mainly wheat, rye and barley.** Oats used to be on that list, as its protein has a very similar structure to gluten, and many people find they react to this as well.

- **Casein is the protein in milk**, present in cow, goat, sheep and human milk and all milk products such as cheese and yogurt.

- **Lactose is the sugar in milk** (a carbohydrate). You can be sensitive to either casein and/or lactose. Lactose gets broken down by processing the milk, whereas casein does not, so if you are lactose-intolerant, some milk products may be tolerated. Mozzarella, Camembert, Emmenthal, Parmesan, sheep cheese are all very low in lactose, as is butter (82).

- **Be aware that gluten, casein and lactose can be hidden in many unexpected foods** such as liquorice, soy sauce and vinegar. Certain flavourings are stuck to food with milk powder or flour. This includes most processed foods, deli meats, margarines, many prepared stocks and soups, frozen chips and soy cheese. Gluten is also used as a binder in some pharmaceutical products.

- **Lactose intolerance is interesting.** Supposedly, it is not a food intolerance at all. The conventional explanation is that people with lactose intolerance can't digest the sugar in milk (lactose) due to the absence of a particular enzyme – lactase - which breaks it down. However, people who lack lactase can still digest lactose with the help of their friends, the gut flora. Some strains of E. Coli present in a healthy gut actually help with this job and break down lactose fully and comfortably (69). This means that if the gut flora is unhealthy, the lactose does not get broken down properly, and you would have to call this a food intolerance after all.

## GUT TROUBLE

**How do we know whether we have a healthy or unhealthy gut?  How do we know if we have food intolerances?**
**We don't, really.**  Symptoms can give us an indication that our bodies are struggling to get the nutrition we need, and as mentioned, they don't have to have anything to do with our tummies at all.  If you find your child gets bloated, tired, cranky, doesn't sleep well, can't concentrate, can't sit still, has allergies, asthma and the symptoms we have mentioned previously, your child may have issues with gut function.

## GUT HEALING

**So what can we do to help their gut heal and restore the gut flora to its natural healthy state?**

Well, first we have to at least minimise or preferably remove the stresses which damage the gut and provide an environment that promotes the good bacteria.
**This means**

- **decreasing exposure to antibiotics and medication,**
- **eating organic and/or pesticide-free produce,**
- **using cleaning products such as vinegar and baking soda,**
- **removing/relieving emotional stresses (as well as possible)**
- **eating a 'gut-healthy' diet.**

I hear you: *'What exactly is a gut healthy diet?'*

Great question, but hard to answer because it is not the same for all of us.

## BLOOD TEST OR NOT?

**An increasingly common, but controversial tool to assess the state of your child's gut health and check for possible food sensitivities is a blood test.**
These can be ordered or performed by your Chiropractor, Naturopath, Nutritionist or Medical Doctor.  The problem with blood tests is that they are just that, blood tests, and the blood is not where you digest your food.  Your food gets digested in your gut.  The nutrients are absorbed through the mucosal tissues and then enter the bloodstream.  As a result, the blood tests for food sensitivities result in very high levels of false positives and false negatives. 'False positive' means that the blood test may show that you are intolerant to a food, when in fact you are not. 'False negative' means that the test shows you are not sensitive, when you actually are.  However, I still think it is not a bad place to start.

I hear you: 'What exactly is a gut healthy diet?' Great question, but hard to answer because it is not the same for all of us.

# ELIMINATION DIET

**Sometimes we need a more comprehensive approach to starve out the bad bacteria and restore the balance of good bacteria in our gut.** The gold standard in testing for food intolerances is the elimination diet. There are different levels to this.

I find removing AFC's (Artificial Additives, Flavouring and Colours) from the diet makes a big difference with a lot of children, including my own. Many find improvement in behaviour and concentration almost immediately. The first few trips to the supermarket will be time-consuming, as you will need to read the fine print on every item. The big eye-catching writing on the front, *'No artificial colouring or flavouring'* usually means there is preservative added. You may need to print out a list of nasties to avoid. There are many small books and handouts available, information is available on many websites, such as fedup.com.au and there are plenty of apps for your phone. Be vigilant with what your child eats - both at home and out - for several weeks to get a chance to observe the change in your child's behaviour and health. Then challenge their system with one of the AFC - let them go all out with colours for a few days and see what happens. Then go dry for a week and try the next one. It is important to just challenge with one additive, flavour or colouring so you know which one she reacts to.

The next level to try would be GFCF (Gluten Free, Casein Free). When our family first tried this long ago, there was no clear labelling on the packages or dedicated aisles in the supermarket. Although it is becoming a much more commonplace diet, it is still not easy, as both gluten and dairy are used so extensively in processed foods. A complicating factor is that both the kids and us adults are psychologically, as well as physically, addicted to the gluten and casein; we feel good when we eat it and rotten when we don't. Giving up our favourite foods is not fun!

There are many, many books, websites, blogs and Facebook pages dedicated to this type of eating, with lots of recipes to make almost every food you care for, with alternative, better- tolerated ingredients. Be aware if you give this a go: cutting down on milk and wheat is not enough. If you want to know how your child truly reacts, you will have to eliminate them completely – no liquorice or soy sauce, or any other foods that contain derivatives of them for about three weeks. Don't decide the diet doesn't work until you have done it wholeheartedly, otherwise you are just wasting your time and effort. Once you know whether it works or not, you can then decide on your level of dedication. The GFCF diet works by stopping the partly-digested molecules resembling morphine, cocaine and heroin from entering your child's blood and brain. It allows the gut flora the chance to heal and recover and the body and brain to function better.

There are other very well-researched elimination diets available which will help your child's gut flora recover and help his upstairs brain function better. Look at Natasha Campbell McBride's 'Gut and Psychology Syndrome' (GAPS for short), Sue Dengate's Failsafe and Monash University's FOD-MAP diets. I would advise not to attempt an elimination diet like that on your own, but to consult with a professional: your Chiropractor, Nutritionist, Naturopath, Bio-Medical Doctor or similar. It is important that your child has a balanced diet to provide all the building blocks for growing, healing and functioning. With a mile-long list of what you cannot and should not eat, it can cause problems both physically and psychologically: *'What do I eat, then?'*

It is important to have suitable healthy alternatives to provide sustenance and nutrients and to satisfy both hunger and cravings. We still have to live life, be happy and involved, go to parties and celebrate. With proper guidance, support and some thoughtful preparation, this is absolutely do-able and so well worth it in the long run when the results are having a happy, functioning, alert, participating, curious, healthy child running around and living life to the fullest.

# MEET **BILLY**

Billy was five years old when he first came in to see me. He was on the 'less functioning' end of the Autistic Spectrum. He was unable to speak, didn't make eye contact, flapped his hands constantly and would very frequently meltdown emotionally, screaming, kicking and carrying on. Mum wasn't looking for miracles; she was just hoping to make him feel better inside. Given his frequent meltdowns, he had had several falls and knocks to the head, which she felt may have caused some issues. Billy didn't look very healthy, either. He was very pale and had big dark circles around his eyes, which is a common sign of food intolerance. His diet was very limited: he only liked soft, white foods like porridge, white bread, milk, yogurt, cheese and pasta.

It was very difficult to care for Billy. I just had to do my best. I would often do his chiropractic adjustments in the reception, under my desk or in the bathroom – wherever he would allow me to. He responded well and became more relaxed and had less temper tantrums.

At this stage, I suggested to Billy's mum that she try to modify his diet. Studies have suggested that children on the Autistic Spectrum tend to be sensitive to gluten and dairy (69, 83). Billy's mum was horrified: *'But what is left for him to eat?'* It wasn't an easy task but she managed to slowly swap to gluten-free and dairy-free varieties of his favourite foods, and the improvements in Billy were astounding! I will never forget the day Billy came in with a drawing to show me. This was a miracle! He was actually sitting at a desk and holding a pen in his hand. He had been there long enough to complete a whole picture and created the most beautiful colourful dragon. I was so excited and proud of him and told him so. Billy turned to me and said: *'It's not a dragon, you dumbo. It's a dinosaur, a Tyrannosaurus Rex!'* Wow, Billy could speak, too. Billy is now fifteen years old and very happy to come in and lie down on my chiropractic bed for a check-up. He is still Autistic and attends a school for kids with special needs. However, he communicates, interacts and learns beyond what anyone had ever dreamed of.

## SUPPLEMENTS

In addition to removing the foodstuffs which interfere with the function of the gut, you will also want to provide nutrients that will help the gut heal. I have listed a couple of recommendations here, but as each person has a unique set of circumstances that has led them to be where they are today, it requires a professional to help make sure you and your child receive the individual healing factors you need. There are so many supplements available that could potentially be of benefit but you don't want to take them unnecessarily, you don't want to take any that work against each other and you want the ones that help you the most at the stage you are at.

Two food supplements that I would recommend to everyone, as they improve digestive function across the board, are bone broths and fermented foods.

**Bone broths** are an excellent source of proteins and minerals and will help your stomach produce the acid it needs to start the digestion process, as well as help the body detoxify. Making a broth is as simple as can be. Use grass-fed, organic, free-range bones of beef, lamb or chicken or non-farmed fish. Add a few vegetables to provide flavour if you wish. Cover bones with water and simmer for about 24 hours. You can drink the broth as is or use it in soups, stews and sauces.

**Fermented foods** contain good bacteria, which help replenish the healthy gut bacteria. You can make them yourself – there are many workshops available to show you how. Fermented foods include homemade yogurts, cottage cheese, sauerkraut, Korean Kim Chi, tempeh, kefir and some table olives.

**Probiotics** You can also buy the good bacteria in a powder form or contained in edible capsules at a health food store. Remember that they don't work well on their own; they need the help of diet modification to starve out the bad bacteria as well. There are many probiotic products on the market, some better quality than others. Look for a brand which contains a mix of many species of bacteria, just like it is in the gut: Lactobacilli acidophilus, Bulgarius and Rhamnosis, Bifido Bacteria Bifidum, Breve and Infantis, Bacillus Subtilis, Escherichia and/or E.Coli.

The supplement also has to contain high enough doses of bacteria to make a difference; at least eight billion per gram. Commercial yogurts and probiotic drinks do not have high enough concentrations of bacteria to be of actual benefit.

*Research shows that children diagnosed with ADHD, autism, depression, dyslexia, schizophrenia and OCD benefit greatly from supplementing with Omega 3 (69).*

**Omega 3** Another supplement I think we need across the board is good fats. The brain consists of 60% fat. The cell membrane around every cell in the body is made up of fat. The protection around the nerves is made of fats. Many neurotransmitters, such as Serotonin, Dopamine and Adrenaline, as well as hormones, are made from fats. Not 'fish and chips' fat, though, but Essential Fatty Acids (EFA), mainly Omega 3. The reason Omega 3 is essential is that our bodies can't make it so we need it from our diet.

Omega 3 is found in:

- cold water fish like salmon
- sardines
- trout and mackerel
- krill and cod liver oil
- flax seeds
- hemp oil
- chia seeds
- rice bran
- green leafy vegetables
- pumpkin seeds
- egg yolks
- grass-fed animal meats/fat
- milk from grass-fed cows

Eating fresh fish a couple of times per week is a great source of Omega 3. However, in children with gut issues, their use of the available nutrients is diminished and will not provide enough available fats. Cooking, canning and curing will deplete the Omega 3.

## ONE STEP AT A TIME

*So the saying 'You are what you eat' is true in more than the straightforward, feeding our cells, sort of way. What we eat also greatly influences the way our brains work with regards to focus, concentration, learning and behaviour.*

This chapter may make you feel overwhelmed or even worried about your child's gut health, and all the difficult changes you may fear you have to put your child through. My advice is, don't worry. You don't have to make all these changes and definitely not all at the same time. Actually, I advise that you don't. This chapter is designed to empower you to ask all the right questions: of yourself - about your lifestyle and the choices you are making for your child – and of your Chiropractor or other health professional. Ask them where to start and how best to do it. With proper guidance and support, you can make one little change at a time. Even if it is choosing to have an apple on the way to school in the morning instead of a processed muesli bar, it is a step in the direction of better health for the body and the brain.

# 5

## Head space and heart space

Remember the first time you held your baby in your arms?  That feeling of awe, love and devotion so strong it almost physically hurt?  When you realised that you would do anything for this little human, at whatever cost to yourself?

**Yes, at this time you are so whacked-out on hormones your brain doesn't work right, but it doesn't change the fact that, no matter what sort of little screamer you have on your hands, you still love him more than anything in the world.**
And love, along with oxygen, movement, stimulation and nutrition, is one of the most important prerequisites for a child's brain development.

One of the hormones affecting our brains at birth is *Oxytocin*, or the 'love hormone', which helps us bond and connect with our new baby.  Oxytocin doesn't just appear at the arrival of a newborn.  It is present throughout our lives, released with hugs, cuddles and pleasant physical touch.

Research has demonstrated that oxytocin affects the *hippocampus*, an area of the brain involved in forming long-term memories and cognitive brain function (84).

A group of researchers compared different types of human touch and found that a loving touch, including caressing and gentle stroking, stimulates the cerebellum more than any other type of touch.  Remember, the cerebellum is crucial for the function of the whole brain, involved in coordination, reading, short-term memory, attention, impulse control and emotional control (85). Another study compared the amount of physical and emotional affection a group of babies received and found that the ones who received the most in infancy had more stable and positive emotional and mental development in their thirties (86). Researchers found that children of mothers who were more sensitive to their needs had better emotional control, behaviour, organisational skills and working memory (87, 88).  And this is not just time and touch from mummy.  Daddy's time, attention, love and affection, particularly through the first year of life, have been shown to improve a child's behaviour later on (89).

> So the more cuddles we give our kids, the better they will do at school and in life.

## LOVE LANGUAGE

*From this research, it is obvious that there are many ways for us to show our kids we love them.*

Gary Chapman, in his book 'Love Languages', talks of five different ways people feel and display love:

» Physical touch
» Words of affirmation
» Quality time
» Gifts
» Acts of service

You may have had this experience yourself.  You've just cooked your child's favourite meal, cleaned up the kitchen, bathed her, organised the school bag and lunch for tomorrow and read her favourite goodnight story.  You tell her it is time for sleep and that you have to finish up something.  Suddenly you find yourself yelled at – screamed at, actually – by your child who says she hates you and that you don't love her and that you never want to do anything she wants to do.  You step back, totally perplexed, wondering where all this came from?  What did you do wrong?

Love is a verb; it is something we do, and people love differently – children included.  In this example, your child feels loved through quality time.  The fact that you choose to go and finish that assignment, instead of choosing to spend time with her may feel like a bucket of ice water in her face.   Although you have just spent a lot of time and energy doing things for her, she may not understand love in that way.  She will tend only to see/hear/feel the time you actively choose to be with her, regardless of the activities.

In this particular case your love language may be acts of service.  You feel you have slaved away for hours doing all the things that need to get done so she gets fed, clothed and cared for.  That is your way of saying *I love you.*

It can be very useful to know your family members' love languages so you can show them how much you love each of them in ways they will understand. It is also valuable for you to perceive the love they show you, even though it is not in your preferred love language. To understand how the rest of your family members feel loved, carefully observe each individual's language, actions and interactions, and soon it will be obvious how they express their love.

The child who tells you how beautiful you are, what a wonderful mother or father you are, calls you endless names of endearment, patiently explains to you how to do things and asks how you think their drawing looks probably feels love through words of affirmation. To feel loved, this child will need a lot of positive feedback and encouragement. For this person criticism can cut very deeply, so guard your words and try to 'sandwich' criticism between positive feedback statements.

If your child gives a lot of cuddles, touches and kisses, enjoys sitting in your lap, massages your shoulders, plays with your hair and uses language about feeling, sensing and touching, chances are this person shows his love through physical touch.

Choosing to spend time with you - rather than doing Lego or playing with friends - by playing a board game, having a conversation about his day, reading a book or even just sitting next to you watching the TV is a display of affection from someone who prefers quality time. For this person, having one-on-one time is essential. This person will revel in your undivided attention even if it's negative, because time spent together is better than no time.

Buying flowers and chocolate is a universal sign of love in our society. Gifts can also be a weed picked from the front garden, a drawing, or a rock found on the street. As parents, we often show children how much we love them by buying the latest expensive toys advertised on TV. This can, however, sometimes backfire, as the child may see it as a way of buying them. They may start demanding things and be unappreciative, as they do not read it as an act of love. A small, thoughtful, personal gift put in a backpack or lunchbox with a small note will be understood and appreciated for what it is – a message of love.

The 'acts of service' love language is the garbage that is carried out, the toys that are put back in the toy-box and the school bag which is emptied. These messages of love are easily overlooked if that's not your language: 'It's your mess' and 'You have to help out. This is not a hotel'. Fair enough! However, to someone with acts of service as their love language, anything you do for them which is a 'sacrifice' of your time and effort will be perceived as an act of love, such as helping them with their homework or doing their dishes.

Knowing the way your family feels your love will help everyone to connect and feel part of the team. It will improve their self-esteem and provide the best grounding for them to blossom in the big wide world.

"There are two lasting bequests we can give our children. One is roots. The other is wings."

~ Hodding Carter

## SELF-ESTEEM

So, as already discussed, love is a verb – something we do, an action, a way of communicating.  However, the love we feel for our child is not because of something she does, no matter how amazing it is.  It is rather for who she is.  We feel and show our love for the 'human being' in front of us, not the 'human doing'.

Research shows that children feel loved when they feel they matter to the world around them; that they make a difference to people, that someone cares, spends time with them and are interested in their lives.  This improves their self-esteem and decreases the risk of violence (90).

As parents, we obviously can and should feel proud and excited about our children's ability, participation and performance.  Heartfelt praise is a very important motivating factor for children (91).  However, over the last many years we have tried to help our children to believe in themselves and to teach them that they can do anything they set their mind to by giving them constant positive feedback.  Research demonstrates that our efforts may not have had the desired effect, though (92, 93), with children shying away from challenges for fear of failure and feeling like they are a failure if they don't achieve their expected outcome.

Henderlong and Lepper, two researchers who have looked into the effects of praise for the past thirty years have made these suggestions:

» Be sincere and specific
» Praise only what they have the power to change
» Use realistic descriptions.  Inflated language can come across as false
» Be careful about praising children for what they love to do and what they find easy
» Encourage kids to focus on mastering skills—not on comparing themselves to others

## MEET **NELSON**

Nelson was eight years old when he first came to see me.  He would trudge in to the practice behind his mother and brother, looking at the carpet, not engaging with anybody, hardly answering greetings or questions. Nelson was seeing me because he was having trouble controlling his bladder.  Not only did he have to wear a nappy to bed - so he had never had a sleep-over- he also had accidents throughout the day.  He would bring spare shorts and undies to school and would change several times throughout the day but he still smelled like urine. The other kids at school called him nasty names and didn't want to play with him or sit next to him in class. Nelson was taking this on board; he was starting to believe he was yucky, filthy, stupid and hopeless.

Nelson's parents had tried everything they could think of to help him: they limited his fluids at night (which can actually increase the concentration of the urine and make the problem worse), they woke him at night to take him to the toilet, they used star charts with big rewards and electronic sensors on the mattress.

They did everything within their might to show him they loved him, that he was good at so many things both at sport and school, that he was a great friend and that his little bladder issue didn't affect the way he was as a person. Unfortunately, it didn't seem to help very much. Nelson was moody, withdrawn and depressed and so his parents' concern had more to do about his mental state than his bladder.

Nelson responded incredibly well to chiropractic care. Within a month he came bounding into the practice, slamming the door against the wall, he was so excited. No need to go and change his pants before he came to lie face down on my table anymore. He was jumping for joy telling me about his upcoming school camp, which he was joining for the first time. It was wonderful to see a spark of life in Nelson.

We still had a lot of work to do though, to change his perception of who he was as a person. We talked about how to question the nasty thoughts that enter our heads uninvited (as we will talk about in a minute) and enlisted the school counselor to help put strategies in place with friendships. It took a few months, but Nelson flourished. His self-confidence improved as he realised what he was capable of and his self-esteem improved as he started connecting and interacting with his peers, making friends and having fun.

# RESILIENCE
## Life is hard!

We will all meet challenges, stress and hardship like Nelson did, and it is not always possible to help or change the circumstances. Losing a friend or family member, parents splitting up, moving schools or hectic family schedules are but a few examples. We just have to learn to deal with life.

According to 'Early Childhood Australia - Research in Practice,' resilience is the group of skills and qualities that lead people, including children, to cope with difficulties in a positive way. Our resilience depends on our personality and problem-solving skills, the opportunities we have for learning skills, the support we receive from our relationships and the resources available in our community.

Parents have an important role to play in teaching our children how to bounce back and thrive. We do this by loving them, showing affection and paying attention, by listening and showing empathy and helping them identify and label their emotions. We also help them by being good role models, showing understanding, compassion and kindness, managing our own stress and emotions and taking responsibility for our own feelings and actions.

Martin Seligman, in his book 'The Optimistic Child', explains that the way we feel about what we experience is based on how we talk to ourselves. Nelson thought that he was dumb and stupid and that no one liked him because he wet his pants.

Seligman suggests that we look at the facts of the situation, question them and keep them in the real world:

» **Personal**: Am I responsible for the situation? (May sound like 'It's all my fault!')
» **Permanent**: Is this the way it will always be? ('I will never figure out how to do this!')
» **Pervasive**: Does it occur in all areas of my life? ('I can't do anything right!')

So, in the case of Nelson:

» **Personal**: I am so stupid I can't even control my bladder.
» **Permanent**: This is the way it has always been and this is the way it will always be.
» **Pervasive**: I can't do anything right and no one likes me.

Talk your child through his sad experience and ask questions about his thoughts and beliefs.

When our thought processes are questioned like this it becomes very obvious that our thoughts play tricks on us, that they are not informing us of the truth. You want to know the real truth? We are not our thoughts! We decide what we think. With some attention and practice we can learn to change what we think, and when we change what we think we change what and how we feel about ourselves and the experiences we have. When we change what we feel about ourselves and our way of being and living, we can choose to be more positive and optimistic. This has been shown to result in longer, healthier and happier lives (94 - 96). The fact is that children learn their explanation style from their parents. So if you want your child to have a longer, healthier and happier life, you know what to do. Practice explaining your experiences in a positive and productive way and help your child learn to think better thoughts about themselves as well.

For example:

» Is it your fault that you can't control your bladder?

» Are you wetting your pants on purpose?

» Do you know for sure that you will be wetting your pants forever and ever?

» Is there a chance that you may grow out of it or that we find a way for your body to work better?

» Does the wetting mean that you are stupid and not capable of doing anything else? I just heard you read a whole chapter of your book to your little brother.

» Does your stubborn bladder mean that you are not a nice and friendly person who likes to play and laugh?

» Did I see you playing and giggling with Grandma just a few moments ago? Do you think she would play with you if you were not a lovely kid?

## TIME

It is not just how to think and how to explain their experiences to themselves that children learn from us; they also learn how to live their lives. We want our children to be happy, healthy, successful, resilient, creative, loving and empathetic human beings. We make it our life's purpose to help them achieve these worthwhile qualities. We feed them nutritious food to grow strong and healthy. We take them to the best schools and help them with homework. We talk to them to try to teach them right from wrong and guide them to make the best choices in life. To encourage them to develop socially, physically, mentally and emotionally, we constantly drive them all over town to sport, music, tutoring, play dates and other pastimes. This is all very important and something we parents can and want to do to help our children succeed in life.

The question is, do we get caught up in the process of providing opportunities? Is it possible that we may have forgotten that many of the important qualities we want our children to have cannot be taught? Connection, self-awareness, imagination and creativity are skills that have to be discovered and developed for ourselves, and learning these takes time: Time that is not parceled up into activities, entertainment and chores, time to do nothing but be, reflect, dream, experiment, connect and discover.

*We are human beings not human doings.*

As parents, we need to trust in our children's innate ability to know and do what is best for him or herself and try not to push our fears for the future on to them.

There is a story of a successful businessman who travels to a remote island to relax and enjoy some fishing. It is a beautiful place with white sandy beaches, bright blue water and palms swaying lightly in the warm breeze, and the fishing is amazing! The businessman is having the time of his life, catching so many fish he doesn't know what to do with them all. He hardly has his line in the water before he has a bite. The businessman thinks this is heaven on earth. Every morning he meets a local man leaving the beach carrying his catch of a single fish. The businessman is intrigued. Has he run out of time? Has his luck run out? One morning he stops and asks the local fisherman why he goes home with just one fish, because he himself catches plenty of fish after the local fisherman has gone home and he would be happy to teach the fisherman some tricks. The local fisherman explains that he doesn't leave because he has to go to work, but that he has caught what he needs for his family today. He is going home to be with his family, play with his children and chat to his friends. The next day they meet again and the businessman excitedly tells him about all the fish he caught the previous day. *'I have had this wonderful idea"* he says. *'There are so many fish here. You should buy a boat, hire some men from the village and catch heaps of fish. You can sell them on the market and make tons of money'.* 'And then what?' asks the fisherman. *'Then, when you have made enough money, you can build a processing factory right here on the beach and ship to the international market. You will be rich!'* 'Then what?' asks the fisherman. *'Then, when you have built it all up in ten or twenty years, you can sell it all to a multinational company, make a huge profit and retire'.* 'And then what?' asks the fisherman. *'Then you can sit back, do a bit of fishing, play with your grandchildren and relax with your friends.'*

Sometimes it seems that we adults are a bit like this businessman, always with an eye on the future, wanting what we see as the best for our kids. Our vision is created from our personal values, experiences and troubles. Our children are like the fisherman, absorbed in the present, doing what needs to be done and enjoying every moment of it. Our children will grow up! They will succeed and prosper in spite of us. Children always have – look at you!

Our children will look to us for guidance on how to live the 'perfect life': what is important, how to communicate and interact and how to strike the right balance. Since we want the best for our kids, how is your life measuring up at the moment? Are you living the life you want your child to copy?

We all try to do and be our best in what we deem to be the important aspects of our lives, including:

- a loving and supportive spouse
- loving, caring parent
- dependable and committed colleague
- helpful and supportive child
- fun and caring friend
- interesting and creative individual
- capable and efficient housekeeper
- interesting and health-conscious cook

All of this, while staying fit and healthy, being socially and environmentally aware, keeping up with current events in the world, looking our best, and the list goes on...

Looking at this list, it really can be a juggle to get the mix just right.

You may feel torn, stressed and/or exhausted trying to do it all and keep everyone, including yourself, happy. Remember that no one actually expects you to be perfect at everything. No one even expects you to do everything - except of course, yourself! It is totally acceptable, even advisable, to make choices to prioritise and say NO THANK YOU – I cannot do this, worry about this or take this on right now. You should come first on your list of priorities. How would it be to spend some quiet time on your own, thinking about and feeling for what it is you want for your life, what your values are and what is most important *right now?*

Write down your thoughts and keep this close at hand so you can have a look every time you make decisions. For example, does the house need to be cleaned for the arrival of the in-laws for dinner right now or is playing with your children more important because you haven't spent fun time with them all day? Is the meeting with your mothers' group more important right now than a quiet evening connecting with your partner? Your physical, mental and emotional health needs, including time to breathe, reflect and play, are at least as important as everyone else's. When you fulfil your needs, you will be much better at supporting others. And if nothing else, this will teach your children to respect themselves and their needs.

# SLEEP

**Rest and sleep are obviously essential for our children's health and wellbeing. We have all experienced the effects of a bad night's sleep or two and recognise the uncomfortable effects of feeling cranky, exhausted and almost crazy. With children, too little sleep has been shown to be associated with hyperactivity, increased anger, aggression and weight gain. The child will often struggle with poor concentration, memory and learning, have more accidents and will tend to get sick more often (97).**

*Sleep promotes physical health, longevity, and emotional wellbeing. Wow, how busy we are while we are off in Never-Never Land!*

Sleep doesn't just prevent those uncomfortable side effects. So many wonderful things take place when we sleep. Our bodies grow, heal, cleanse, rejuvenate and regenerate. Our brain processes, organises and stores what we have experienced and learnt through the day so we can access the information later. Our immune system, hormones and digestive system work their wonders.

I know that it is redundant telling you now that a good sleep routine for your child is important. Like me, you have known this since your child was a baby.

According to the Sleep Health Foundation this is the recommended amount of sleep for children:

| AGE | RECOMMENDED HOURS | MAY BE APPROPRIATE | NOT RECOMMENDED |
|---|---|---|---|
| 0-3 months | 14-17 | 11-13 | Less than 11 |
| | | 18-19 | More than 19 |
| 4-11 months | 12-15 | 10-11 | Less than 10 |
| | | 16-18 | More than 18 |
| 1-2 years | 11-14 | 9-10 | Less than 9 |
| | | 15-16 | More than 16 |
| 3-5 years | 10-13 | 8-9 | Less than 8 |
| | | 14 | More than 14 |
| 6-13 years | 9-11 | 7-8 | Less than 7 |
| | | 12 | More than 12 |
| 14-17 years | 8-10 | 7 | Less than 7 |
| | | 11 | More than 11 |

Please note that these recommendations are for a 24 hour period. It is normal for children to have daytime naps until three to five years old. If a child takes naps often past this age, she might not be sleeping enough at night.

*'Great', I hear you say 'And just how am I to get her to get that amount of sleep?' - That is the Million Dollar question!*

First of all, remember that our sleep and wake cycles are controlled by hormones in our bodies and that these follow an inner rhythm that may be a little bit different in all of us, and that is ok. Observe what your child's individual sleep - wake rhythm is and work with that.  Encourage your child to have the same bedtime and same wake-up time every day to promote a good sleeping routine, and if you find your child is not getting enough sleep, set a consistently earlier bedtime every day.

There are two main hormones involved in the sleep-wake cycle: *Serotonin* and *Melatonin*. Serotonin calms you down and melatonin induces sleep.  Both hormones are light-sensitive, meaning as we get to the end of the day and the natural sunlight fades, the serotonin levels increase and it converts into melatonin, which makes you go to sleep.  Serotonin is made from an amino-acid called *Tryptophan*, which we get from many foods: turkey, tuna and other meats, soy protein, walnuts, brown rice, bananas, avocado, spinach, dairy products, starchy carbohydrates like potatoes, carrots and grains all contain tryptophan.  Vitamin B6 is used in the synthesis of tryptophan. B6 is found in sunflower seeds, pistachios, wild tuna, turkey, pork, beef and chicken, dried fruits and bananas, so make sure your child's diet includes these foods.

As the sleep hormones are light-sensitive, it is very helpful to make the difference between night and day as clear as possible.  Help your child to get exposed to real light through the day by playing outside, walking/riding to school and doing homework in a space which gets as much natural light as possible.  This does not necessarily mean exposure to direct sunlight, but being in natural light rather than electrical light sources.  The opposite counts at night: dim the lights, draw the curtains and avoid screen time for at least one hour before bedtime.

We sleep better when we are physically tired and both exercise and fresh air are great for that. Encourage your child to get plenty of physical activity every day to burn off energy and be ready to rest.  Exercise stimulates the brain in the short term, so it is best to do this earlier in the day.  If your family likes yoga and Tai Chi, they actually help to calm the nervous system.  Avoid strenuous exercise for four hours before bedtime; so if the kids enjoy wrestling with dad, try to get that done before dinner...

To help getting into a calm relaxed state prior to bedtime, start slowing down activities one to two hours before bed.  Take a relaxing and soothing bath or shower and do quiet activities together such as reading books, telling stories, drawing, breathing exercises, meditation, doing craft or a puzzle.  A cup of chamomile tea can be very relaxing.  If your child is ok with dairy, a cup of warm milk has also been shown to help promote sleep.  Avoid putting sugar in the drink as that tends to increase activity levels in the short term. It is also best to not eat a lot just before bed as the digestion may interfere with sleep.  If your child is hungry, give him a light snack, ideally a food containing tryptophan to help produce serotonin. A protein snack is better than a carbohydrate as it provides energy for longer. Avoid caffeinated drinks for several hours prior to bedtime.

If your child has trouble sleeping due to anxiety, or wakes from nightmares, it is important that you talk about what is concerning her, but address this earlier in the day.  Just prior to bedtime you are better off getting your child to think about happy places and things, like going to the park or Grandma's house.

This pre-sleep time is an important time not to use screens such as TV, computer, iPad or phones. These devices emit colours, which stimulate our waking brain and keep it active, which is what we wish to avoid at this time.  For this reason - and many more, as discussed earlier - it is also advisable not to have TV's or computers in children's bedrooms.  Also, we are creatures of habit and we want the brain to associate the bed with sleep, not with game playing and socialising.

Prepare for bed by having your child's bedroom free of toys and clutter; we don't want our children to get inspired to play at this time. Keep the room dark and cool. Have a night light on if that helps your child feel safe and comfortable.

According to the National Health Service in the UK, children who don't sleep enough can display behaviour similar to children with ADHD: overactivity, seeking constant stimulation, irritability and difficulty with concentration. Tired children also have a higher risk of being overweight or obese due to craving starchy and sugary food to help them stay awake through the day. A study released in Pediatrics in 2012 showed that kids whose bedtime was moved to an hour earlier slept on average 27 minutes more per night. This was associated with their teachers reporting them to have better behaviour, more empathy and being more alert (98). Research also shows that children with ASD or ADHD tend to struggle with sleep, which can exacerbate difficult behaviour (99, 100).

Too much sleep can be as bad for our energy levels as sleeping too little. Excess sleep in children has been associated with depression, anxiety, upper respiratory complaints, asthma and obesity (101).

It is normal for teenagers to change their sleep patterns and want to stay up late and then sleep all day. It is not (just) because they are lazy, there are actual biological reasons for this (102). One is that the melatonin release happens later at night in this age group, so they are not actually tired at 'normal' bedtime. However, their changing brains and bodies still need a lot of sleep to grow and develop at this age, so they are exhausted and can't get up in the mornings after too few hours in bed. There is currently a push in the US to start high school later in the day to accommodate these young people's brain function so they can learn, behave and function at *their* best, not ours! This doesn't mean you as a parent should just sit back and let them play on the computer or watch videos all night. Given that our school system does not accommodate late sleepers, you will need to try to negotiate workable bed times so he can still function the next day. Particularly for this age group, it is essential that the screen is turned off at a sensible time.

# JUST BREATHE!

Another essential for life and brain function for both big and little people is the air we breathe. We need oxygen for our bodies, muscles, organs and cells to work. The brain is particularly 'hungry' for air. It comprises of just 2% of our body total weight, but consumes about 20% of our oxygen. And how do we get oxygen? Well, we breathe, of course. No big deal really, it happens automatically every few seconds, right?

Unfortunately it is a big deal and many of us don't breathe very well or effectively. The main breathing muscle, our diaphragm, sits between the bottom of our lungs and the top of our gut and is affected by our posture, health, muscle strength and flexibility and fitness levels. Try this little experiment. Sit on a chair in the most slumped-over position you can get to, as if you are twelve years old and have been playing on your phone for hours. Now take a deep breath in. How did that feel? Next, sit up nice and straight; spine straight, shoulders back and head up, as if you have just had a wonderful invigorating walk. Take a deep breath in. What do you notice? Obviously, taking a breath in when you are straight is much easier and you can inhale a lot more air. When we slouch, we are unable to fully contract the diaphragm and open the lungs to get in a full breath of air. Instead, we use the smaller, secondary breathing muscles in the neck, shoulder and chest to expand the lungs, often causing these muscles to get strained and sore. Since these muscles are situated at the top part of our bodies, they cannot replicate the work of the diaphragm and get air into the bottom of our lungs. The resultant lack of oxygen supply has serious detrimental effects on brain function and our health as a whole.

So what can we do to change? Having mum remind us all the time to sit straight and breathe properly doesn't seem to work very well. Taking some time out to consciously breathe is a good idea.

**Here are some ideas:**

- In my experience, chiropractic care can be of great benefit, by improving both the nervous system function and the movement of the ribcage and spine.

- Have your child sit or lay comfortably with both hands on her stomach. If lying, she can place a small toy or special rock on the stomach to have something to focus on. Ask her to take a breath all the way into the stomach and concentrate on the feeling of the stomach, and not the chest so much, rising. Exhaling fully, she should feel the stomach flattening again. She should focus on getting the air all the way down into the bottom of the lungs where she can feel it against her hands. Children may find it easier to concentrate when counting the length of the breath: breathe in for four heart beats, hold for four and breathe out for four.

- Some of us are very restricted in our breathing pattern because our chests and diaphragms are really tight. A great way to release this is to lie on a Pilates foam roller or three tightly rolled up towels (lay the towels flat, one on top of the other, then roll them tightly to make one big roll). Lie down on the roll so it is going along the spine with the head, spine and tailbone supported. Rest the hands on the floor, palms up and allow your shoulder blades to relax down towards the floor. You should feel your chest stretching, your lungs expanding and that you are able to take a deeper breath. Ahh, that is wonderful! Now guide your child to do the same.

- Encourage your child to hang with straight arms on the jungle gym or from the top of a door frame or a chin-up bar to stretch the chest and diaphragm. Remind your child to concentrate on just holding on with his hands and allowing the shoulders and body to relax and stretch. Hopefully he can feel the diaphragm relaxing and stretching, letting him take a deeper breath.

*Breathing slowly and deeply helps to improve our overall health, immune function, mood and concentration and helps to calm us down.*

# MEDITATION

The physiological aspect of breathing helps us sustain our cells and keep us alive as well as calming our nervous system. Mindfulness and meditation are the next natural steps up from this (I will use these terms interchangeably). Meditation is the practice of concentrated focus upon a sound, object, visualization, the breath, movement, or attention itself in order to increase awareness of the present moment (103). As science catches up on this ancient practice, the benefits of meditation are omnipresent, and not just for adults. When looking at meditation for children, it has been found to help them feel calm, improve focus, concentration and memory, reduce stress, strengthen immune function, decrease aggression and anxiety and improve behavior, attitude and relationships. In one study they looked at a group of seven to nine year old children who practiced mindfulness for thirty minutes twice a week. These kids experienced significant improvement in attention, behaviour and memory after just eight weeks of practice (104). Another study looked at the effect of mindfulness sessions in 500 twelve to sixteen year olds leading up to exam time. The kids who participated in the sessions felt significantly less stress and depression and a greater sense of wellbeing compared to their non-participating peers. Furthermore, the more frequently the students practiced mindfulness, the better their academic achievement in exams (105).

The thought of children meditating is wonderful. And yes, realistically it is easier said than done. You obviously can't just send them to their room to meditate, as they would (as a rule) have no clue. Set some time aside for you to have this lovely calming and bonding experience together with your child, maybe before going to bed or as they first wake up. There are many websites, apps, blogs and books available advising and demonstrating how to do it and many provide free guided meditations for children. The trick is to start out gently and not to expect too much. Two minutes is better than no minutes.

*"Expect nothing - be grateful for everything"*

~ *Unknown*

In this chapter, the main message is basically to trust in your child's innate ability to grow up into a 'perfect' human being.  She will – supported by your unconditional love and attention - find ther way, given the time and space.

**Khalil Gibran says it so well:**

*"Your children are not your children.*
*They are the sons and daughters of Life's longing for itself.*
*They came through you but not from you and though they are*
*with you yet they belong not to you."*

# 6

## Switched-on Kids

*"You can discover more about a person in an hour of play than in a year of conversation"*

*~ Plato*

Play is essential for your child's development.

What may look like whiling time away is actually one of the most brain-stimulating activities a child can do, contributing to cognitive, physical, social and emotional wellbeing.

As a matter of fact, play is so important for optimal child development that it has been recognised by the United Nations High Commission for Human Rights as a right of every child.

# PLAY

Child-directed play is what a child will do when no-one is watching and telling or suggesting to them what to do and they have the free space to do it in. This is a natural impulse and definitely not a waste of time. Play is children's work! This is how a child learns about themselves and their world. Unsupervised play obviously doesn't mean you allow them to be unsafe, but rather to provide the opportunity for the kids to make their own rules and decisions.

During unstructured play children will create and explore a world they can master, taking the size steps they know they can handle to ensure their success. This helps to develop and improve confidence and resilience and allows them to work on their fears. They learn how to work in groups, to share, to communicate and negotiate, to resolve conflicts, to care for others and to learn self-advocacy skills. They learn the art of non-verbal communication: how to move, posture and position themselves, as well as use facial expressions to express their intent and be able to read it in others. Are we playing or fighting? Are you friend or foe? When kids play by themselves or in groups they practice decision-making skills, move at their own pace, discover their own areas of interest and ultimately, engage fully in the passions they wish to pursue (106).

Child-directed play doesn't mean you as a parent are excluded from this fun. Far from it! Playing with your children is a wonderful way to connect, to make them feel safe, loved and cared for. Just follow your child's instructions, let your hair down and enjoy the fun and games they come up with.

The importance of play is increasingly being recognised by researchers and policy makers as essential for a child's emotional and intellectual development. Despite this knowledge, many countries, including Australia, encourage earlier introduction to formal learning (107), with preschools teaching what was traditionally taught in kindergarten and year one. Already Australian children start school at a younger age than most of the developed world (108). Interestingly, three of the best performing locations with regards to literacy are Singapore, Shanghai and Finland, where kids start school at age seven years or older (108).

Research has shown that delaying children's school start by one year (start by age seven) decreases their risk of inattention and hyperactivity at the age of eleven by 73% (109). This improvement in behaviour is attributed to an extra year of playtime. One study showed that children who were allowed to play while in preschool had better grades by year six (twelve years old) than peers who were introduced to formal learning earlier (110). Studies have also shown that eleven year old children have the same reading ability whether they start formal learning by five or seven years of age (111). However, children who started learning younger had poorer reading comprehension and enjoyment.

> There really is no doubt about the importance of play in brain development.

# Out of doors

Outdoor play in particular has decreased considerably over the past 20 years, despite being so essential for children's health and wellbeing. The average child now spends less than thirty minutes a day enjoying unstructured outdoor play (112). This trend is at least partly to blame for the huge increase in overweight and obese children, along with the associated health risks we are experiencing in the Western world (113). Being outside improves our children's levels of Vitamin D, which will increase the bone density and decrease the risk of future heart disease and diabetes (114). Playing out of doors helps exercise the eyes by making them change focus frequently and appears to decrease the occurrence of near-sightedness (115, 116) and blindness (117). Research has shown that playing in natural surroundings such as parks, gardens and school recreational areas which have dirt, rocks, trees, shrubs and water, such as creeks and lakes, improves children's strength, flexibility and coordination and reduces their stress levels and inattention. It also fosters supportive relationships and feelings of competence (118) and improves learning (119). Children diagnosed with ADHD experience improvement in their behaviour from being in nature (120).

# SCHOOL

*"Children today are tyrants. They contradict their parents, gobble their food, and tyrannise their teachers"*

Socrates, the Greek philosopher from Athens, said these words 2400 years ago, which then begs the question whether we actually have an epidemic of learning and behaviour problems today. Or are we creating a 'disease' out of normal childhood behaviour because it doesn't support our lifestyle? Is the media keeping us informed and empowered or creating a fear in parents of our children not performing well enough? Is our current system of childcare and school set up to support, stimulate and develop our children to be their best?

If you look at our school system from a historical perspective, it is based on the needs of an agricultural society where we needed the next generation to be willing to knuckle down and continue what we had started. I would argue that we are teaching our children to listen and do as they are told, like soldiers responding to a superior; herded together in age groups for many hours in a row, expected to sit still, or to move at the teacher's or the school bell's discretion and perform tasks that can at times seem rather pointless for future life skills and happiness.

However, if you go back to the way we learnt prior to that, in hunter-gatherer societies, for hundreds of thousands of years, we learnt by play, observation, exploration and mimicry. We were with people of different ages and skills from our own family and village. We learnt what was needed to survive by active participation rather than theory, lectures and staged examinations. This seems like a more holistic way of learning.

We don't live in a hunter-gatherer society, though. We have to, by law, teach our children to read poems and do calculus. Research shows that better literacy skills are strongly associated with a healthy and happy life (121). So I am not suggesting you opt out of society. What I am saying is, let's use some common sense. Let's try not to worry so much about our children's early academic success or the constant demands on their lives and just let them live a little. Do you know what the most accurate predictor of academic success in primary school children is? Come on, make a guess. High socio-economic background? Better teachers? Eating veggies? Consistent completion of homework? Read on, you will be surprised!

> Do you know what the most accurate predictor of academic success in primary school children is? Read on, you will be surprised!

# HOMEWORK

**Is homework necessary for academic success?**
We adults think it is an integral part of going to school and learning well. Teachers tell me that it is the parents who ask for homework for their children, to help them get ahead. So while the conventional answer is 'yes', I am going to point out a few studies which put the importance of homework for our children's learning into perspective.

» According to a 2012 Australian Institute of Family Studies media release, 95% of Australian ten to eleven year olds get homework. In USA, the proportion of six to eight year olds who were assigned homework every night went from 34% in 1997 to 64% in 2002. The children of that age more than doubled their homework load in that time period, however the increase in homework was not associated with any increase in scores on achievement tests (122, 123).

» Several researchers have concluded that there is very little correlation between the amount of homework and academic performance in primary school (124, 125, 126), and it is only effective when there is an adult around to ask for help when needed (127).

» A 2014 parliamentary inquiry from the Department of Education and Early Childhood Development in Victoria found strong evidence "and general agreement" that homework had almost no academic benefit for primary school students, although it may help prepare them for secondary school. This followed a report by the NSW Department of Education with a similar conclusion.

» Many countries with the highest scoring students on achievement tests such as Japan, Denmark, and the Czech Republic, have teachers who assign little homework. Meanwhile, countries such as Greece, Thailand, and Iran, where students have some of the worst average results, have teachers who assign a lot of homework (128).

So if homework is not the answer for helping kids do better at school, what else can we do? Our aim is to encourage them to be curious and interested in learning and the world around them. This is how:

» I've mentioned this several times already: 90% of stimulation to the brain comes from movement of the spine. Our brains work better when we move regularly – we concentrate better, think clearer, focus on tasks, get ideas, find solutions and so on. Walking, running, biking, swimming, playing tips, throwing a football, jumping on a trampoline, climbing a tree, rolling down a hill, balancing on a log, crawling through bushes, playing soccer, tennis and netball. – these are all fantastic ways to supercharge our brains with stimulation! Anything and everything helps! So after sitting for six hours at school, it is time to get outside and move.

» Playing an instrument and singing are both powerful stimulators of the brain and both have been shown to increase concentration and learning ability (129).

» Having meals together as a family is the single strongest predictor of better achievement scores and fewer behavioural problems for children aged three to twelve years old. This was the conclusion of a national survey in the USA conducted by the University of Michigan. They found family meals were a better predictor of achievement scores than the amount of time spent studying (130). Family meals improve literacy (131), academic performance (132, 133) and mental and emotional health (134).

The American Educational Research Association states that:

*"Whenever homework crowds out social experience, outdoor recreation and creative activities, and whenever it usurps time that should be devoted to sleep, it is not meeting the basic needs of children and adolescents".*

# HOMEWORK HELP

### *Given that we can't fight it, we'll join it - sensibly!*

**Here are some tips for homework that may help at least the parents:**

- Remember whose homework it is! Encourage, help, motivate, brainstorm, be a sounding board - but don't *do* the work. Let your child be responsible for the time, effort, completion and rewards/consequences

- Read with your child every day

- For overall brain function, exercise regularly, eat nutritious food and get enough restful sleep

- Talk to your child and ask his opinion about important topics to help stimulate the brain, focus, reason and formulate thoughts

- Let your child see you do your homework every day: reading, paying bills, reading, completing tasks, reading, working on the computer, and don't forget - reading.

- Be realistic about the amount of time your child can concentrate. According to The Student Coalition for Action in Literacy Education, a child's attention span for a specific task is almost the same in minutes as their age in years.

- Establish a good study routine: Set up a calm, clean, light learning space with as few distractions around as possible and set time aside daily/weekly for using this space.

- Switch off non-essential electronic devices for the specified study period, including music, Internet, games, phones, iPads, laptops (as well as washing machines, oven timers, etc).

- If you struggle to get your child to do the given homework task, let him play outside for some time to burn off some energy and focus the brain.

- Be clear on what you want to achieve in a study session. Bigger assignments are better chunked into smaller, more manageable tasks, which are easier to start and complete in one concentrated session.

- Lao Tzu said, *"A journey of a thousand miles starts with a single step"*, so just do it! Start and the rest will follow.

- Have regular breaks - not breaks to do more of the same, like playing on the computer, but something different. Move, stretch, walk, drink some water, eat an apple and some nuts or have a conversation.

- If it becomes a fight, leave it. It is not your responsibility! Your loving, caring, nurturing and supportive relationship with your child is too important. Ask the teacher for strategies which can help.

- **And lastly and probably most importantly, celebrate that good feeling of having completed the set tasks. Tell them what a star student they are!**

# MEMORISING

Homework often involves memorising (boring!) stuff like sight words, multiplication tables, spelling words and French verbs.  Some people find that easy, others don't - including me. This is a real issue – converting information into long-term memory and knowledge which can be accessed on demand.  The most common way to get information into long-term storage is through repetition.  By repeating the same thing over and over, you are creating a new, specific pathway of nerve impulses in the brain, a pathway that can become a highway by frequent use.

If I were to ask you to tell me a memory, any memory from your life, what would you say? Would you describe your happiness and excitement as you walked down the aisle with your father about to be married?  The wonder and amazement as you counted the fingers and toes after the birth of your first child?  Perhaps the horror and defencelessness as that motorbike came screeching around the corner out of control, just before it hit your car.  As you will notice, what these memories all have in common is a strong emotion.  An experience is really just a combination of sensory information such as sights, sounds, tastes, smells, the feel of things and balance.  This sensory information is just facts – it is neutral – but as our brains attach emotion to it, it gets processed differently and then enters long-term parking in the brain, specifically the Mammalian Brain.  I am sure you had no trouble remembering the above events.

We can use this knowledge of how memories are made and stored to our advantage when it comes to learning in a school situation.

It takes a bit of effort and preparation on the parent's part, but is it not worth it to see your child succeed?

*Here are some suggestions to help your child learn and memorise information:*

- When you help you child with her homework, present the information through as many senses as possible. Tell your child about the information and explain the logic of it. Let your child see it in pictures or words, let him play with it, construct it and let him try to get his body to look like it. For example, with a particular spelling word like 'school,' talk about school and what happens there, get your child to write the word and let them draw a picture of it. Cut the word into individual letters and let him make it as a puzzle. Let your child play with the letters and make new words. Let him play school and position his body both like the shapes of the letters in the word and the building itself.

- Stimulate the other senses while trying to memorise information. For example, introduce a smell like cinnamon, citrus or vanilla while practicing spelling or times tables. Eat something special and different, or enjoy having a back scratch or a hand massage while working. Each sensory stimulus will make an association that creates an emotion that will make it easier to recall. When your child is at school, they will be able to visualise the sensory pattern and access the memory through this visualisation.

- Another way of creating a memory is by making up a story. For example: 'My brother and I went for a walk. Our four cute little feet were stepping on the soft grass in the yard. Here they met eight little nasty green ants that were looking for food. *'Look at all this food',* yelled the hungry green ants to their friends, and they came to look too, so now there were 12. They scrambled on to the cute little feet and took a big bite or two, 16 painful bites all together. *'Ouch',* my brother and I screamed as we ran home and put all twenty little toes in the bath to make them feel better'.

- Make a song. Use your favourite tune to make a silly song containing what you need to remember. Whether it is the shopping list, the French verbs or the spelling list, this works a treat. You don't even have to sing it out loud; humming it in your head will do when you have to remember the facts at school.

- Write down what you have to remember, for example spelling words, in a single colour on different coloured palm cards. Practice the task with your child using the palm cards. You might find they keep forgetting the 'h' in night. On a different palm card, highlight or write in a bright colour the 'h' in night to trick the brain into paying extra attention to that one while you keep practising.

- I have mentioned this one before and it is my favourite. Let your child do an activity like bouncing a ball, skipping rope, jumping on a trampoline, balancing on one foot or even tapping a foot or a finger while practicing spelling words or his times tables. The task has to be simple, easy and repetitive enough for the child not to have to concentrate on the task, but only what is being memorised.

*Most importantly, have FUN. Make it enjoyable and light. No one will learn anything when they are cranky, upset, defensive or sobbing. Let your creative juices flow, change your homework help games often and just love your child for who she is!*

# LEARNING STYLES

As mentioned, I am not very good at remembering things by heart. I struggle to remember details such as numbers and people's names and I am close to hopeless with a map, following directions, recipes and instructions. I am good at remembering concepts though. I am also good at reading and grasping the big picture and I think I am good at explaining what I have understood.

We all have strengths and weaknesses like that, both with regard to how our brains work and more specifically, how we learn.

Imagine a hot iron. This is dangerous equipment and should be kept out of young children's reach. How would you learn this?

1. Your mother explained to you not to touch the iron because it was very hot and you would burn yourself.
2. You saw your sister touch the iron and burn herself, and you learnt not to do that.
3. You went to the hot iron after having been told and even after seeing your sister burn herself, and you very carefully and briefly just had a tiny little feel with one finger; you burnt yourself and learnt not to do that again.

These are three different styles of learning:

**HEARING      SEEING      MOVEMENT**

The fact that people learn in different ways was introduced by Howard Gardner, an American psychologist, in 1983. He proposed that there are different facets to our intelligence and that a balance of these leads to a person who is highly functioning in life and society (135):

**Howard Gardner's Theory of Multiple Intelligences:**

**VERBAL-LINGUISTIC:**
The ability to use words and language for reading, writing, memorising and telling stories.

**LOGICAL-MATHEMATICAL:**
This is about logic, abstract thoughts and reasoning, as well as the use of numbers and the recognition of abstract patterns.

**VISUAL-SPATIAL:**
The ability to visualise objects and spatial dimensions, and create images and pictures in the mind's eye.

**BODY-KINESTHETIC:**
The wisdom of the body and the ability to control physical motion and timing in making things, sports, dance and acting.

**MUSICAL-RHYTHMIC:**
The ability to sing, play an instrument or compose music, and have a sensitivity to sounds, rhythms, beats and tonal patterns.

**INTERPERSONAL:**
The capacity for person-to-person communications, relationships and cooperation and being highly sensitive to other people's moods, feelings, temperaments and motivations.

**INTRAPERSONAL:**
Awareness of inner states of being and understanding own thinking, values and beliefs.

**Gardner later added two more types of intelligence:**

**NATURALISTIC:**
Being able to recognise flora and fauna and relating to the natural environment.

**EXISTENTIAL:**
The spiritual aspects of intelligence.

Only the first two are highly valued in schools. However, children have a unique blend of intelligences and Howard Gardner argues that our education system's ultimate goal should be to help the child find her talents and teach her to explore and expand these. Also, nine kinds of intelligence give us nine ways to teach rather than one. A concept should be introduced in many different ways, thereby helping to increase the number of children who grasps the concept.

I remember trying to help Signe with multiplication, something her teachers and my husband and I had covered many times before, but a concept she continually struggled with. One day I suddenly heard myself saying to her:

*'Now, listen carefully to what I am saying. Pay really close attention to my words. You walk down to the shop to buy four ice creams. Then, you go again to buy four more. And again, you buy four more. How many ice creams did you buy altogether?'*

I know I am very auditory and that was why I was trying to teach Signe that way. That's how I learn best. However, Signe is not auditory at all. She learns best by visual means and movement. She needs to see it and feel it. I know that. But I got caught up in ME. And her teachers were teaching thirty kids, and explaining is the easiest way to teach thirty kids at once. Once I grabbed the matches and we had three piles of matches with four in each, we started getting somewhere. Just because Signe couldn't follow my explanation doesn't make her stupid, dyslexic or slow. As adults, we should welcome the challenge to find a way to explain a concept so that the child can understand in their own unique way.

Daniel Goleman later suggested that we should also consider Emotional Intelligence (EQ). He was wondering, similarly to Gardner, how people with a lower IQ appeared to be able to do as well in life as people with high IQ. Goleman states that our feelings around an outcome are fundamental to our future actions. For the experience of taking a test at school to have more value over time, it is not as important how she performs in the test as how she feels about the result. If the child has a low emotional intelligence and performs poorly, they will likely give up. *'I can't do this. I studied and failed, so I might as well not even give it a go. I am useless!'* A child with a more positive EQ may get the same poor result but think: *'All right, that was a bad result. I obviously didn't study the right material in the right way. I didn't put in enough time to understand the concepts and the information properly, or I simply had a bad day. I will have to try something different next time. I'll ask my friend and my teacher to help me do better next time.'* Goleman concludes that our school system can improve the way it teaches us to deal with stress and failure to facilitate our mindset of perseverance, and that challenges, knockbacks and failures are just stepping stones on the path to success in the game of life.

> *No matter what type of learner your child is, you will find that your child will do better if you explain the WHY behind what he is being asked to learn.*

## MULTITASKING

**For mothers, multi-tasking is a bit of a survival instinct. How else are we going to fit it all in? While we are driving the kids to soccer, remembering to pick up the pet supplies on the way, we are on the hands-free phone organising ballet pickup and writing a mental list for the grocery store as well as refereeing the war happening on the back seat. Sound familiar?**

If he understands the big picture and the purpose of what he is trying learn and achieve, it is going to make more sense why he is putting in time and effort instead of doing something he would rather do, like playing or chatting. Why do we need to know our times tables? We can just use the calculator on the phone if we want to know what four times three is, right? However, it would be really handy to know how to multiply in your head when you try to figure out how much the ice creams cost, especially if you want to ask your mum for the money.

Or when the bin needs to be carried out, instead of saying: *'Because I asked you'*, it may work better to explain: *'When the bin is full, it starts to smell in the kitchen and that attracts flies. Flies lead to maggots, and I'd rather have maggots in the wheelie bin than in the kitchen, thank you.'*

Interestingly, while we think we are so effective, the truth about multi-tasking is that not only do we frequently 'drop the ball' and mess something up completely, we actually get a lot less done in the available time. Research shows that multi-tasking means that a job takes 50% longer and we make 50% more mistakes than if we concentrate on one thing at a time (136, 137).

Unfortunately, our children are picking up our bad habits, with lifelong repercussions. They do their homework while chatting to friends on Facebook, emailing, listening to music and playing games online, and as a result, it takes longer and they learn less.

Our brain is only capable of doing one thing at a time, that's just the way it is wired. Like your computer, it is able to have many windows open at the same time, but you can actually only actively work at one window at a time. We can go from one window to the next, however our effectiveness slows when we shift focus from one task to another.

The brain is wired sequentially, so when the brain has to shift focus, the following has to happen: First, it has to send certain messages to tell the part of the brain working at that particular moment to stop doing what it is doing (for example, the English essay). Then it has to send messages to another part of the brain to get that part to work (for example, 'What are my mates up to tonight?'). Then, when that's all sorted out and we want to refocus our attention back to where we were, we have to send messages to tell the 'mate' part of the brain to stop, and new messages back to the 'English Essay' part to get it focusing again. This is incredibly time consuming. It actually takes 7/10 of a second to switch between tasks, and although that does not seem like much, it all adds up.

If we want to be fast and effective learners we have to stop multi-tasking, and do just like our mothers suggested: *'Focus on one job at a time'.*

# MEET **SOPHIA**

*Sophia came to see me because her parents were concerned about her posture.*

She looked weak and uncomfortable as she sat in my office, slouched over with her chin sticking out like a little turtle. During the initial case history conversation it also came to light that Sophia struggled with learning at school. She was ten years old and had received extra help at school with reading and maths since kindergarten, and had recently started tutoring in both topics after school as well.

Sophia had been a very happy and lazy baby who was content to lie around and observe the world. She had never rolled, had spent very little time on her tummy and she was late at learning to sit, crawl and walk. Her parents had used a Bumbo seat to help her sit and a Jollyjumper to help her stand and exercise her legs.

When I checked Sophia's posture, I compared her to what good posture looks like, which is:

> **FROM THE BACK**
>
> - Shoulder height even on both sides
> - Waist and hips level side to side
> - Weight distributed evenly through both feet
> - Head and neck straight on top of the spine and tailbone

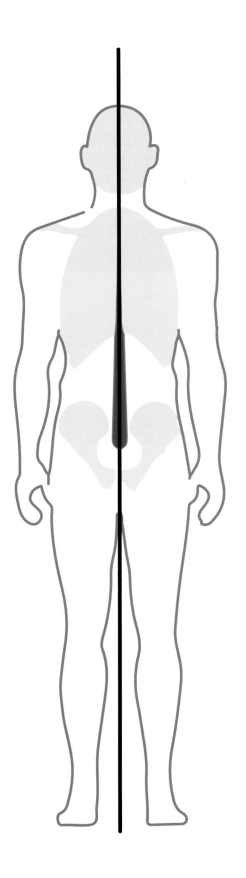

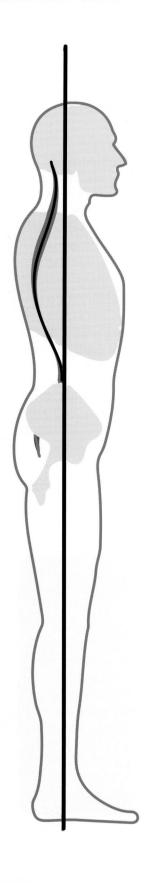

**FROM THE SIDE**

- Ear should be in line with the middle of the shoulder vertically

- Shoulders directly over hips

- Hips over knees over anklebones

- Three normal, natural curves of the spine, meaning forward curve in neck and lower back and backwards curve in the middle back.

*This is an important checklist, so make sure you assess your child's posture straight away.*

Sophia's head was in front of her shoulders and the shoulders rolled forward. She had a swayback, pushing her pelvis and belly forward, her toes were pointing in and her left hip and shoulder were higher than the right. (Sophia also had trouble balancing and coordinating her movements and had a subluxation in the bottom part of her skull).

You may remember that the cerebellum is the part of the brain which controls your posture and muscle tone and it is also very involved in your ability to learn and concentrate; I suspected it was the cerebellum that was not working well in Sophia.

How did this happen? It's hard to know, but her early lack of movement may have had something to do with it. Tummy time is the most important exercise babies can do as it develops their core strength, which every other movement from then on depends on. The hard work tummy time requires helps to stimulate the brain, especially the cerebellum, and ensures that muscle tone is set properly.

Using equipment which helps a child perform a skill they can't as yet do themselves means they don't get enough time to practice and perfect that skill, and this can lead to future weaknesses in movement control. Babies, infants and kids often absolutely love using such equipment, but their bodies aren't ready for those postures and movements. For example, using the Bumbo seat helped Sophia sit before she had the core strength to hold herself upright and balanced, so she never needed to learn to use her abdominal muscles properly. This may have contributed to the delay or absence in her other gross-motor skills.

# POSTURE

Sophia is not alone with posture struggle. Research shows that up to 90% of people experience poor posture (138) and it has far-reaching effects for our health:

- The American Journal of Pain Management states: *"Posture affects and moderates every physiologic function, from breathing to hormonal production. Spinal pain, headache, mood, blood pressure, pulse and lung capacity are among the functions most easily influenced by posture."* (139)

- Dr Roger Sperry, the Nobel Prize winner in Physiology in 1981 states: *"The more mechanically distorted a person is, the less energy is available for healing, metabolism and thought."*

- In his book 'Rejuvenation Strategy', Rene Cailliet, MD, writes that poor posture with the head on a forward angle can add up to 14 kilos of extra strain on the neck. This can lead to improper spinal function, compress the internal organs and decrease lung capacity by up to 30%. Our ability to learn, concentrate and remember all depend on this oxygen supply, and proper spinal function.

- Recent research shows that in infants, having a straight spine actually improves their ability to map new experiences and remember details (140).

- Good posture affects your mood, making you feel more energetic, positive and happier (141). You also have more confidence in your own thoughts (142) and feel more powerful (143). Body posture also influences the levels of stress hormones in your blood (143).

Our sedentary lifestyle is one of the main issues for posture. On average, 50% of an Australian's day is spent sitting (144). Now **Our sedentary lifestyle is one of the main issues for posture.** On average, 50% of an Australian's day is spent sitting (144). Now that's a lot! From a health perspective, sitting down for prolonged periods without a break slows the processing of fats, glucose and other substances. This increases the risk of developing chronic disease, even when recommended levels of physical activity are met.

Did you know that 'Sitting is the new smoking?' It is the 'hot' media slogan right now, and for good reason. Recent research (145) shows that for every hour we watch TV (or sit with the iPad, laptop or phone), our life expectancy decreases by 22 minutes. Given the average child spends 7.5 hours per day in front of a device, not including school computers, this is shaving more than six years off your child's life over their lifetime! This is a bigger threat to life expectancy than being morbidly obese or a smoker. Smoking one cigarette is estimated to shorten life expectancy by 11 minutes, which is equivalent to 30 minutes of TV watching (146).

### So what to do to help Sophia?

As you are well aware, reminding children to sit and stand up straight has not been very successful in the past. Chiropractic adjustments, as I have mentioned many times already, are about allowing the brain and body to connect as well as possible to monitor what is going on, to integrate the information and then tell the body to perform in a certain way. Sophia improved a lot when we adjusted her neck, both with her posture and her ability to learn at school. I also showed her some balance and shoulder exercises to help the cerebellum work better.

You might also find these exercises really helpful.

## Superman

Have your child lie over the exercise ball on her stomach. Initially, keep the feet shoulder width apart on the floor to create a solid base. With the arms down along the sides of the body, lift the upper body up off the ball. You want to see a straight line from the feet to the head. Hold for 30 seconds. Progress the exercise by extending the arms straight out to the sides and then straight out in front, in line with the rest of the body.

Next, roll forward on the ball so the hands can touch the floor and the feet are in the air. Again, you want your child to be in as straight a line from the head to the toes as possible. Hold for 30 seconds. To increase the challenge, roll further forward so more weight is on the arms and the core muscles have to work harder to keep the body straight.

The next step is to have both hands and feet off the floor. Start by lying tummy down on the ball, hands and feet touching the floor, if possible. While a parent is stabilising by holding the child gently around the waist/lower back, ask the child to lift the head up in line with the spine and with both arms and legs off the floor to make a straight line and balance there for as long as possible.

*When your child is comfortable, you can progress the exercise by just supporting the ball, not your child.*

## Balancing on one foot

Get your child to stand in a clutter-free corner of a room. Facing into the corner, ask him to lift his hands up to shoulder height so they are close to the wall but not actually touching it. Lift one leg up, and when comfortable, close both eyes. Your child may get really wobbly, and if so, instead of putting the foot down and starting again, just have him catch himself by lightly touching the wall until he feels balanced again. Then let go and keep concentrating on being straight and strong. Stay like this for 30 seconds, then swap legs and try the other side. This is very hard to do when slouching so doing this exercise will help the cerebellum to subconsciously straighten the posture to help make it easier to balance. The side-effect?
A straighter spine without having to consciously think about it.

## Angel

Have your child standing with her back against a wall. With upper arms at shoulder height, flex the elbows to 90 degrees with both hands and elbows touching the wall. Slowly raise the arms to bring the hands together above the head. Once the hands meet, slowly glide the arms down again until the elbows touch the sides of the body. Repeat ten times.

# SWITCHED-ON KIDS

*So here we are at the journey's end. I thank you for being here with me.*

We started out by wishing for happy, healthy, successful, creative and empathetic children and here you are now with a toolkit bulging with ideas, tips and exercises to help your child achieve these qualities. Your child may need a lot of help or maybe just a little. Either way, you now have the tools to take an active role in making a difference in his life.

Albert Einstein once said that the definition of insanity is doing the same thing over and over again and expecting different results. He also said we can't solve problems by using the same kind of thinking we used when we created them. Unfortunately, that is exactly what we do when we realise our kids are struggling at school: teacher's aides, after school tutors and extra homework. The solution may be more forthcoming if we step back and assess how best to help our child from a *different angle*. It is this change in perspective that worked so well for my daughter and the children I see in my practice, and what I have tried to explain to you throughout this book.

In the Brain chapter we talked about how neuroplasticity – the brain's ability to make new connections between nerves and to forge pathways – is the way we learn everything. Using this fact gives us the opportunity to do something we are good at and, through this, to stimulate areas in the brain, which may not be connecting so well.

We looked at the pyramid of brain development, where our ability to use the thinking brain on the top (neocortex) to our optimum potential depends on our earlier ability to perform and harness our movement patterns and emotional control, which are both functions from the younger child's brain. This journey of brain development is essential for our learning success.

We discussed how we can activate those neurological pathways in the pyramid of learning at any age through exercise and movement and how chiropractic adjustments help the brain make better connections and decisions.

In the chapter about food we explored the presence of our second brain and how to feed it well and keep it healthy so it can strengthen the function of our first brain.

We emphasised the importance of a parent's love and attention on a child's development, focus and learning, at the same time keeping in mind that our children are not us, and that they have their own destiny to fulfil.

Lastly, we looked at how we can help our children succeed within the established school system by keeping them the centre of our teaching focus rather than a cog in the wheel of an education system.

The solution to your child's success lies in one or a combination of the ideas I have shared with you. You may find your child gets wonderful results from just one missing link. You may find that your child needs a bit more help than that. A combination of approaches will increase the results of your efforts manifold. If this all seems a bit overwhelming, what I would suggest is to choose three things you want to change. Now, pick one small, simple thing that you can do immediately, and give it enough time and love. Then move on to the next one on your list, and then the next.

Just remember that healing takes time. Learning takes time and miracles *do* happen, but usually they are underpinned by hard work and perseverance. The result may not be exactly what you envisioned. We are not all destined to be Einsteins or maths professors. We are destined to find our strengths and make the most of them in every area of our lives.

I hope you now feel that this is a journey that you are ready to undertake with your child and to explore the possibilities of his or her great success potential. You can help to switch your kid on, one little step at a time!

Dorte

# 7

## Where it came from

"Become who you are!"
~ Friedrich Nietzsche

# CHAPTER 2

1. Bower, J.M. and Parsons, L.M. Rethinking the 'lesser brain'. Scientific American

2. Melillo, R. and Leisman, G. Neurobehavioral disorders of childhood (2004). New York, New York: Springer Science

# CHAPTER 3

3. Chaddock-Heyman, L., et al. The effects of physical activity on functional MRI activation associated with cognitive control in children: a randomized controlled intervention. Frontiers of Human Neuroscience. (2013) (7)

4. Åberg, M., et al. Cardiovascular fitness is associated with cognition in young adulthood. National Academy of Sciences, Vol. 106, (2009) Dec

5. Trudeau, F. and Shephard, R. Physical education, school physical activity, school sport and academic performance. Int J Behav Nutr Phys Act. (2008) (5)

6. Kamp, C.F., et al. Exercise reduces the symptoms of Attention-Deficit/Hyperactivity Disorder and improves social behaviour, motor skills, strength and neuropsychological parameters. Acta Paediatrica, Volume 103, (2014) July

7. Cerrillo-Urbina, A.J., et al. The effects of physical exercise in children with Attention-Deficit/Hyperactivity Disorder: a systematic review and meta-analysis of randomized control trials. Child Care Health Dev, (2015) May

8. Hoza, B., et al. A randomized trial examining the effects of aerobic physical activity on Attention-Deficit/Hyperactivity Disorder symptoms in young children. J of Abnormal Child Psychology, (2015) May

9. Archer, T., et al. Physical exercise alleviates ADHD symptoms: regional deficits and developmental trajectory. Neurotoxicity Research, (2012) Feb

10. Sowa, M. Effects of physical exercise on autism spectrum disorders: a meta-analysis. Research in Autism Spectrum Disorders, Volume 6, (2012)

11. Lang, R. Physical exercise and individuals with autism spectrum disorders: a systematic review. Research in Autism Spectrum Disorders, (2010) Oct-Dec

12. Oriel, K.N., et al. The effects of aerobic exercise on academic engagement in young children with autism spectrum disorder. Pediatr Phys Ther, (2011) Summer

13. Cannella-Malone, H., et al. Using antecedent exercise to decrease challenging behavior in boys with developmental disabilities and an emotional disorder. J of Positive Behavior Interventions, (2011) Oct

14. Pan, C.Y., et al. Effects of water exercise swimming program on aquatic skills and social behaviors in children with autism spectrum disorders. Autism, (2010) Jan

15. Whyte, S. Screen-addicted children may have newest mental illness. Sydney Morning Herald, (2012) Sept 30

16. Ko, C.H., et al. Brain activities associated with gaming urge of online gaming addiction. J of Psychiatric Research, (2009) Apr

17. Lin, F. and Zhou, Y., et al. Abnormal white matter integrity in adolescents with internet addiction disorder: a tract-based spatial statistics study. PloS One, (2012) (7)

18. Christakis, D., et al. Early television exposure and subsequent attentional problems in children. Pediatrics, (2004) Apr

19. American Academy of Pediatrics: Committee on Public Education. Children, Adolescents, and Television. PEDIATRICS, (2001) Feb

20. Brown, A., Shifrin, D. and Hill D. Beyond 'turn it off': how to advise families on media use. AAP News, (2015) Sept 28

21. Zero to Eight - children's media use in America 2013. A Common Sense Media Research Study, (2013) Autumn

22. Planinsec, J. and Pisot R. Motor coordination and intelligence level in adolescents. Adolescence, (2006) Winter

23. Westendorp, M., et al. The relationship between gross motor skills and academic achievement in children with learning disabilities. Research in Developmental Disabilities, (2011) Nov–Dec

24. Brookes, R.L., et al. Striking the right balance: motor difficulties in children and adults with dyslexia. Dyslexia, (2010) Nov

25. Chang, Y.K., et al. The impacts of coordinative exercise on executive function in kindergarten children: an ERP study. Exp Brain Research, (2013) Mar

26. Budde, H. and Voelcker-Rehage, C., et al. Acute coordinative exercise improves attentional performance in adolescents. Neuroscience Letters, (2008) Aug

27. Reynolds, D. and Nicolson, R.I., et al. Evaluation of an exercise-based treatment for children with reading difficulties. Dyslexia, (2003) Feb

28. Reynolds, D. and Nicolson, R.I., et al. Follow-up of an exercise-based treatment for children with reading difficulties. Dyslexia, (2007) May

## CHAPTER 4

29. Australian Institute of Health and Welfare 2011-12: Overweight and Obesity.

30. Health and Social Care Information Centre: Statistics on Obesity, Physical Activity and Diet - England, (2015)

31. www.cdc.gov/nchs/fastats/obesity-overweight 2011-12

32. Sundhedsstyrelsen (Danish Health and Medicines Authority) (2010)

33. Rietmeijer-Mentink, M., et al. Difference between parental perception and actual weight status of children: a systematic review. Matern Child Nutr, (2013) Jan

34. USDA Role of Nutrition in Learning and Behavior: a Resource List for Professionals. (2011) August

35. Donin, A.S., et al. Regular breakfast consumption and type 2 diabetes risk markers in 9 to 10 year-old children in the Child Heart and Health Study in England (CHASE): A Cross-Sectional Analysis. PLOS Medicine, (2014)

36. Rampersaud, G.C., et al. Breakfast habits, nutritional status, body weight, and academic performance in children and adolescents. J Am Diet Assoc, (2005) May

37. Holloway, C.J. A high-fat diet impairs cardiac high-energy phosphate metabolism and cognitive function in healthy human subjects. Am J Clin Nutr, (2011)

38. Gillette-Guyonnet, S., et al. Caloric restriction and brain function. Curr Opin Clin Nutr Metab Care, (2008) Nov

39. Castelli, D.M., et al. Physical fitness and academic achievement in third and fifth-grade students. J Sport Exerc Psychol, (2007) Apr

40. Johnson, R.K., et al. Dietary sugars intake and cardiovascular health: a scientific statement from the American Heart Association. Circulation, (2009) Sept

41. Green Pool Commodity Specialists. Sugar consumption in Australia: a statistical update.

Brisbane, QLD, (2012) October 4

42. Prinz, R.J., et al. Dietary correlates of hyperactive behavior in children. J. of Consulting and Clinical Psychology, (1980) Dec

43. Johnson, R.J., et al. Attention-Deficit/Hyperactivity Disorder: is it time to reappraise the role of sugar consumption? Postgrad Med, (2011) (123)

44. Blunden, S.L., et al. Diet and sleep in children with Attention-Deficit/ Hyperactivity Disorder: preliminary data in Australian children. J Child Health Care, (2011) (15)

45. Howard, A.L., et al. ADHD is associated with a "Western" dietary pattern in adolescents. J Attention Disorders, (2011) (15)

46. Wiles, N.J., et al. "Junk food" diet and childhood behavioural problems. J Clin Nutr, (2009) April

47. Soffritti, M., et al. The carcinogenic effects of aspartame: the urgent need for regulatory re-evaluation. Am J Ind Med., (2014) Apr

48. Abu-Taweel, G.M., et al. Cognitive and biochemical effects of monosodium glutamate and aspartame, administered individually and in combination in male albino mice. Neurotoxicol Teratol., (2014) Mar-Apr

49. Swithers, S.E. Artificial sweeteners produce the counterintuitive effect of inducing metabolic derangements. Trends Endocrinol Metab, (2013) Sept

50. Yang, Q. Gain weight by "going diet?" Artificial sweeteners and the neurobiology of sugar cravings. Neuroscience, (2010)

51. Nettleton, J., et al. Diet soda intake and risk of incident metabolic syndrome and type 2 diabetes in the Multi-Ethnic Study of Atherosclerosis (MESA). Diabetes Care 32, (2009)

52. EAFUS: Everything Added to Food in the United States. Food and Drug Administration, (2011) Nov

53. A Current Affair. (2005) June

54. Kidd, P. Attention Deficit/Hyperactivity Disorder (ADHD) in children: rationale for its integrative management. Altern Med Rev., (2000) (5)

55. The Feingold Association of the United States

56. http://www.truthinlabeling.org/hiddensources.html

57. Eady, Julie. Additive Alert - Your guide to safer shopping. (2nd edition) (2010)

58. Arnold, L.E., et al. Artificial food colors and attention-deficit/hyperactivity symptoms: conclusions to dye for. Neurotherapeutics, (2012) July

59. No author credited. Artificial food colouring is associated with hyperactivity symptoms in children. Prescrire Int., (2009) Oct

60. Mpountoukas, P., et al. Cytogenetic evaluation and DNA interaction studies of the food colorants amaranth, erythrosine and tartrazine. Food and Chemistry Toxicology, (2010) Oct

61. Mikkelsen, H., et al. Hypersensitivity reactions to food colours with special reference to the natural colour annatto extract (butter colour). Arch Toxicol Suppl, (1978)

62. Food dye: a rainbow of risks. Center for Science in the Public Interest

63. IARC: International Agency for Research on Cancer. Monographs evaluate consumption of red meat and processed meat. WHO (2015) October

64. Growtheer, et al. Sulfites: separating fact from fiction. University of Florida, Family Youth and Community Sciences, (2014) June

65. McCann, D., et al. Food additives and hyperactive behaviour in 3-year-old and 8/9-year-old children in the community: a randomised, double-blinded, placebo-controlled trial. Lancet, (2007) Nov

66. Lau, K., et al. Synergistic interaction between commonly used food additives in a developmental neurotoxicity test. Toxicological Sciences, (2006) Mar

67. Stevenson, J., et al. The role of histamine degradation gene polymorphisms in moderating the effects of food additives on children's ADHD symptoms. Am J of Psychiatry, (2010) Sept

68. Gershon, Michael, D., MD. The Second Brain. Harper Collins

69. Campbell-McBride, Natasha, MD. Gut and Psychology Syndrome.

70. Dominguez-Bello, M.G., et al. Delivery mode shapes the acquisition and structure of the initial microbiota across multiple body habitats in newborns. PNAS, (2010) June

71. Neu, J. and Rushing, J. Cesarean versus vaginal delivery: long-term infant outcomes and the hygiene hypothesis. Clin Perinatol, (2011) June

72. Guaraldi, F. and Salvatori, G. Effect of breast and formula feeding on gut microbiota shaping in newborns. Front Cell Infect Microbiol, (2012) (2)

73. Hasselbalch, H., et al. Breast-feeding influences thymic size in late infancy. Eur J Pediatr, (1999) Dec

74. American Academy of Pediatrics website: healthychilden.org

75. Hanson, L. A. Session 1: Feeding and infant development breast-feeding and immune function. Proc Nutr Soc, (2007) Aug

76. Belfort, M.B., et al. Infant feeding and childhood cognition at ages 3 and 7 years: effects of breastfeeding duration and exclusivity. JAMA Pediatr, (2013) Sep

77. Victora, G., Horta, B.L., et al. Association between breastfeeding and intelligence, educational attainment, and income at 30 years of age: a prospective birth cohort study from Brazil. Lancet Global Health, (2015) April

78. Bailey, L.C. Association of antibiotics in infancy with early childhood obesity. JAMA Pediatr, (2014)

79. CDC Morbidity and Mortality Weekly Report, (2011) Sept. 2

80. Kennedy, P. The fat drug. The NY Times, (2014) March 8

81. Casas, L., et al. Domestic use of bleach and infections in children: a multicentre cross-sectional study. Occup Environ Med, (2015) April

82. www.sanslactose.com

83. Autism Research Institute

# CHAPTER 5

84. Owen, S.F., et al. Oxytocin enhances hippocampal spike transmission by modulating fast-spiking interneurons. Nature, (2013) Aug

85. Crucianelli, L., et al. Bodily pleasure matters: velocity of touch modulates body ownership during the rubber hand illusion. Frontiers of Psychology, (2013) Oct

86. Maselko, J. Mother's affection at 8 months predicts emotional distress in adulthood. J Epidemiology and Community Health, (2010) July

87. Kok, R., et al. Parenting, corpus callosum, and executive function in pre-school children. Child Neuropsychology, (2014) Volume 20

88. Landry, S.H., et al. Responsive parenting: establishing early foundations for social, communication, and independent problem-solving skills. Dev Psychol, (2006) July

89. Nordahl, K. Dad is important for his children's development. KILDEN - Information Centre for Gender Research in Norway, (2014) Sept

90. Elliott, G. Perceived mattering to the family and physical violence among adolescents. J Family

Issues, (2011) April 23

91. Henderlong, J. and Lepper, M.R. The effects of praise on children's intrinsic motivation: a review and synthesis. Psychol Bull, (2002) Sept

92. Brummelman, E. On feeding those hungry for praise: person praise backfires in children with low self-esteem. J Experimental Psychology, (2014) Vol. 143

93. Corpus, J.H. and Lepper, M.R. The effects of person versus performance praise on children's motivation: gender and age as moderating factors. Educational Psychology, (2007) Aug

94. Tindle, H.A., et al. Optimism, cynical hostility, and incident coronary heart disease and mortality in the women's health initiative. Circulation, (2009) Aug

95. Cohen, S., et al. Positive emotional style predicts resistance to illness after experimental exposure to rhinovirus or influenza A virus. Psychosomatic Medicine, (2006) (68)

96. Positive Thinking: stop negative self-talk to reduce stress. Mayo Clinic

97. Blunden, Dr. Sarah. Sleep Health Foundation

98. Gruber, R., et al. Impact of sleep extension and restriction on children's emotional lability and impulsivity. Pediatrics, (2012) Nov

99. Lamm, Dr. Carin. Sleep and Autism Spectrum Disorder (ASD) at 'Autism Speaks'

100. ADHD and Sleep in children. Sleep Health Foundation

101. Calhoun, S.L., et al. Prevalence and risk factors of excessive daytime sleepiness in a community sample of young children: the role of obesity, asthma, anxiety/depression and sleep. Sleep, (2011) Apr

102. Backgrounder: Later school start times. National Sleep Foundation

103. thefreedictionary.com

104. Flook, L., et al. Effects of mindful awareness practices on executive functions in elementary school children. J of Applied School Psychology, (2010) (26)

105. Kuyken, W., et al. Effectiveness of mindfulness in schools programme: non-randomised controlled feasibility study. Br J of Psychiatry, (2013) Aug

## CHAPTER 6

106. Gleave, J. and Cole-Hamilton, I. A literature review on the effects of a lack of play on children's lives. Play England, (2012) Jan

107. Whitebread, D., et al. The importance of play: a report on the value of children's play with a series of policy recommendations. Written for Toy Industries of Europe (TIE), (2012) April

108. McNeilage, A. Experts warn starting school too young harms learning, wellbeing. Sydney Morning Herald, (2014) Jan 26

109. Dee, T. and Sievertsen, H.H. The gift of time? School starting age and mental health. National Bureau of Economic Research Working Paper No. 21610, (2015) October

110. Marcon, R. Moving up the grades: relationship between pre-school model and later school success. Early Childhood Research & Practice, (2002) Vol 4

111. Suggatea, S., et al. Children learning to read later catch up to children reading earlier. Early Childhood Research Quarterly, (2013) Vol 28

112. Wen, L.M., et al. Time spent playing outdoors after school and its relationship with independent mobility: a cross-sectional survey of children aged 10–12 years in Sydney, Australia. Intl J Behavioral Nutrition and Physical Activity, (2009) (6)

113. Trost, S., et al. Physical activity and determinants of physical activity in obese and non-obese children. Int J Obes, (2001) Vol 25

114. Mansbach, J.M., et al. Serum 25-Hydroxyvitamin D levels among US children aged 1 to 11 years: do children need more vitamin D? Pediatrics, (2009) Nov

115. Rose, K., et al. Myopia, lifestyle, and schooling in students of Chinese ethnicity in Singapore and Sydney. Arch Ophthalmol, (2008) (126)

116. Sherwin, J.C., et al. The association between time spent outdoors and myopia in children and adolescents: a systematic review and meta-analysis, Ophthalmology, (2012) Oct

117. Holden, et al. Prevalence and pathologies of high myopia. Mlvision, (2015) 28 July

118. Chawla, L., et al. Green schoolyards as havens from stress and resources for resilience in childhood and adolescence. Health & Place, (2014) July

119. Wells, N.M. At home with nature: effects of "greenness" on children's cognitive Functioning.

Environment and Behavior, (2000) Vol 32

120. Kuo, F., et al. A potential natural treatment for Attention-Deficit/Hyperactivity Disorder: evidence from a national study. Am J Public Health, (2004) Sept

121. Australian Government Policy Brief. Literacy in Early Childhood. (2008) No 13

122. Hofferth,S. and Sandberg, J.F., How American children spent their time. J Marriage and Family, (2002) Feb

123. Hofferth, S. Changes in American children's time – 1997 to 2003. Electron Int J Time Use Res, (2009) Jan 1

124. Cooper, et al., Does homework improve academic achievement? A synthesis of research, 1987-2003. Review of Educational Research, (2006) Spring

125. Kohn, Alfie. The Homework Myth: why our kids get too much of a bad thing. (2006) Gallup Press

126. Hattie, John. Visible Learning: a synthesis of over 800 meta-analyses relating to achievement. (2009) Routledge

127. Hoover-Dempsey, K., et al. Parental involvement in homework. Educational Psychologist, (2001) Vol 36

128. Baker, D. and LeTendre, G. National differences, global similarities: world culture and the future of schooling. (2005) Stanford University Press

129. Kraus, N., et al. Engagement in community music classes sparks neuroplasticity and language development in children from disadvantaged backgrounds. Front Psychol, (2014) (5)

130. Fruh, S., et al. The surprising benefits of the family meal. J Nurse Practitioners, (2011) Jan

131. Snow, C.E. and Beals, D.E. Mealtime talk that supports literacy development. New Dir Child Adolesc Dev, (2006) Spring

132. Larson, et al. Forms and functions of family mealtimes: multidisciplinary perspectives. New Dir Child Adolesc Dev, (2006) Spring

133. The Importance of Family Dinners V. The National Center on Addiction and Substance Abuse at Columbia University, (2009) Sept

134. Eisenberg, M., et al. Correlations between family meals and psychosocial well-being among adolescents. Arch Pediatr Adolesc Med, (2004) (158)

135. Gardner, Howard. Frames of Mind: The Theory of Multiple Intelligence. (2011) (1st ed 1983) Basic Books

136. Medina, John. Brain rules. (2008) Pear Press

137. Ophir, E., et al. Cognitive control in media multitaskers. PNAS, (2009) July

138. Posturing for wellness. Good health begins with good posture. Journal of the American Chiropractic Association, (2001) May

139. American Journal of Pain Management, (1994) (4)

140. Morse, A., et al. Posture affects how robots and infants map words to objects. Plos-one, (2015) March 18

141. Peper, E. and Lin, I. Increase or decrease your depression; how body postures influence your energy levels. Biofeedback, (2012) Autumn

142. Petty, R., et al. Body posture affects confidence in your own thoughts. Research Dept: Ohio State University

143. Carney, D. and Cuddy, A. et al. Power posing: brief nonverbal displays affect neuroendocrine levels and risk tolerance. Psychol Sci. (2010) Oct

144. The Chiropractic Association of Australia

145. Veerman, et al. Television viewing time and reduced life expectancy: a life table analysis. Br J Sports Med, (2012) Vol 46

146. Shaw, M., et al. Time for a smoke? One cigarette reduces your life by 11 minutes. BMJ, (2000) Jan